NEVADA BUREAU OF MIN
SPECIAL PUBLICATION 19

GEOLOGIC AND NATURAL HISTORY TOURS IN THE RENO AREA

by

Becky Weimer Purkey and
Larry J. Garside

Illustrated by Kris Ann Pizarro

1995

Mackay School of Mines

UNIVERSITY
OF NEVADA
RENO

How to use the Trip Guides

Directions are given as "right" or "left" and as clock directions; for example, 12:00 is straight ahead and 9:00 is to the left.

Turnoffs to key roads, exhibits, etc. are noted at many mileage points.

On the longer trips you will be instructed to reset the odometer to 0.0 at some places along the route; this makes it easier for you to chose or omit portions of the trip and also reduces errors caused by variations in odometer calibration.

The text descriptions at mileage points should be read by a passenger so that the driver can devote proper attention to driving.

Most of the trips are fairly close to services, should you need them, except for parts of Trip D. Be a prepared traveler. Carry extra water, maps, appropriate clothing for Nevada's notorious changing climate, tools for emergency car repair, first aid kit, and signaling devices.

Please help protect the fragile environment of these mountain and desert areas and items related to its historical antiquity. Leave only footprints and, above all, enjoy this magnificent area!

For definitions of terms used in the text please refer to the Glossary in the back of this book. The Bibliography, also located at the back of this book, provides a warehouse of additional sources of information on the topics covered in the trip guides.

Contents

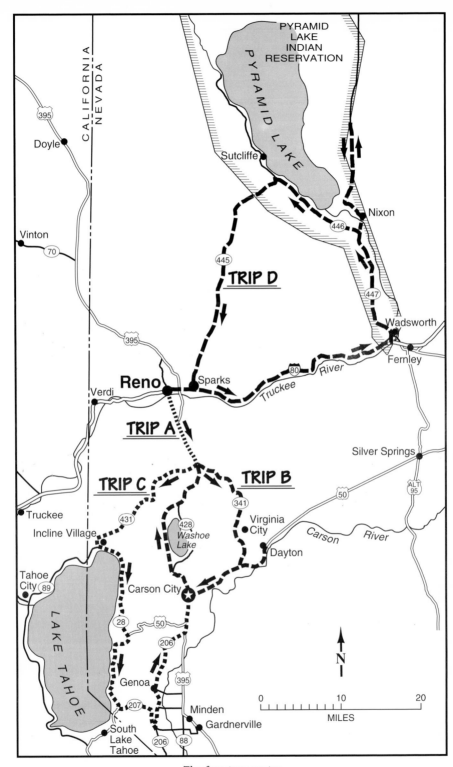

The four tour routes.

4

Preface

Much of the research performed by the staff at the Nevada Bureau of Mines and Geology (NBMG) and the Bureau of Land Management (BLM) is published in technical reports that are useful mainly to earth scientists; however, there are many people fascinated by the intriguing landscapes in the Reno-Lake Tahoe-Pyramid Lake areas who would not normally be aware of these reports, nor enjoy wading through the technical language in them.

This book is intended to fill gaps in the current collection of available publications on tourist attractions and the natural history of the Reno-Tahoe area. The goal is to provide a geologic guide for local citizens and tourists as they drive the main roads visiting the area's many sites of natural beauty and historical importance. We hope that this volume will also provide area schools with earth science information and ideas for field trips and field study areas. If you want to know more about this area's landscapes, geologic history, cultural history, rock formations, and mineral deposits, you will enjoy this publication.

Four trips are offered in this book. Total mileage and information on services along the routes are given in the introduction to each trip. Trip A guides the traveler through the center of Reno and is an introduction to the glacial and seismic history of the area. Trip B highlights the mineral formation and mining history of the Comstock Lode in the Virginia Range southeast of Reno. From Virginia City, the routes of the early gold panners, emigrant trails to California, the Pony Express and the Virginia and Truckee Railroad are followed into Carson City and then north through Washoe Valley and sites of ore and lumber milling towns that supported the Comstock mines. This trip ends at Steamboat Hot Springs geothermal area just south of Reno. Trip C climbs up the Mount Rose Highway on the east slope of the Carson Range southwest of Reno to the Tahoe Basin. A dramatic change in the vegetation zones will be discussed along the way to Lake Tahoe. Trip D departs east from Reno and Sparks through the Truckee River canyon to Pyramid Lake, a remnant of vast ancient Lake Lahontan, and an area possessing a rich culture of the Paiute Nation.

ACKNOWLEDGMENTS

We are grateful to the individuals and organizations that contributed their knowledge, talents, services, and finances to the preparation of this publication.

This book is a synthesis of information based on the research and writings of many scientists and historians who dedicated many years of their lives to studying and documenting the natural and human history and prehistory of this fascinating area. They are listed in the bibliography. Their work has helped reveal the story behind the great natural beauty of this area where earthquakes, volcanoes, glaciers and climate have interacted to shape the landscape, form the rocks and the mineral and energy resources, and determine the local vegetation and animal life. The human history of the Paiutes and their ancestors, the early explorers and emigrants, and the miners—and the silent remnants of the mines and mills and railroads of the "rush to Washoe"—are just as intriguing.

Without the generous financial support of the BLM, this guidebook would not have been published. We especially want to thank Thomas Leshendok and Neal Brecheisen of the Reno office for recommending this project for funding and supporting it to its completion.

Cynthia Pinto and Jim McLaughlin of the Reno BLM office rode along on the first run of the trips sharing their knowledge of the Paiute culture and the soil and vegetation types. Neal Brecheisen of the Reno BLM office and Jonathan Price, Jim Rigby, and Dick Meeuwig of NBMG traveled every mile with Becky Purkey providing valuable comments on the geology and text.

Thomas Lugaski of the Mackay School of Mines shared his knowledge of the vegetation patterns in the Great Basin and of the alteration of volcanic rocks in the Steamboat and Geiger Grade areas (Trip B). The results of the work by Donald Hudson, consulting geologist, were also used heavily for the geology of the Comstock Lode (Trip B).

Steve Castor helped write the Introduction. Kris Pizarro produced the excellent maps, illustrations, and sketches. Dick Meeuwig edited the text and figures and Rayetta Buckley composed and typeset the final product.

We especially want to thank the knowledgeable individuals who read the manuscript and made valuable suggestions that substantially improved the final product: Phillip Earl of the Nevada Historical Society; Maureen Leshendok of the University of Nevada, Reno; John Bell, Jon Price, and Joe Tingley of NBMG; and Neal Brecheisen, Cynthia Pinto, and Jim McLaughlin of the BLM.

Photos are by Becky Purkey unless otherwise noted. Historical photos were reproduced with permission from the Nevada Historical Society and the W.M. Keck Museum (UNR).

Introduction

Regardless of the season or time of day, the majestic desert-mountain setting of the Reno area offers continuous respite to residents and visitors from the cares of life and provides an endless selection of recreational opportunities. The youthful and rugged scenery—the mountains, canyons, valleys, playas, lakes, and landslides—results directly from geologic processes of rock formation, tectonic forces active in the crust of the Earth, and erosion. In short, the scenery is geology.

Geology is also the dominant influence on other characteristics of the land, including water and soil distribution, that ultimately determine where and how plants and animals live. Geology is an important factor in the human environment, as well. Early human inhabitants lived where they could find water, food, and natural shelter. Most of the more recent (last 150 years) human settlements were built adjacent to sources of water or valuable mineral deposits. Before we construct modern shelters—especially in this area—we must take into account the availability of potable water; possible earthquake, landslide, or flood damage; and climate and soil type for those dependant on ranching or agriculture.

Reno is in the Basin and Range physiographic province, a region characterized by a series of generally north-trending mountain ranges and intervening valleys filled with sediments. The Carson Range, an offshoot ridge of the Sierra Nevada just west of Reno, is in the transition zone between the Basin and Range province and the Sierra Nevada province (refer to Trip C).

The Reno area is particularly good for the study of geology, especially earthquakes and faulting, volcanic rocks, precious-metal ore deposits, geothermal activity, and the effects of glacial erosion and deposition. The rocks in this area range in age from Mesozoic (occurring as roof pendants surrounded by granite in certain mountains) to Pleistocene (occurring as basalt flows and glacial lake deposits tens to hundreds of thousands of years old) and Holocene (occurring as alluvial deposits along streams). Tectonically, it is an active region; seismologists monitor continuously for indications of adjustments in the Earth's crust. The rocks and faults are well exposed over large areas because there is sparse vegetation and soil cover over most of this area.

The portion of the Basin and Range province north and west of the Colorado River drainage was named the Great Basin by John C. Frémont in 1844. It covers most of Nevada, about one-third of Utah, and parts of California, Oregon, and Idaho. It is a vast closed basin in which practically all streams eventually terminate in valleys having no external drainage, forming ephemeral ponds (playas) or perennial lakes. Trip D to Pyramid Lake clearly illustrates this type of drainage.

Elevations in the Reno area range from about 3,780 feet at Pyramid Lake to 10,776 feet at the peak of Mount Rose in the Carson Range.

Local climatic conditions are influenced largely by the barrier of the Sierra Nevada. Most storms come from the Pacific Ocean to the west and northwest, but occasional summer storms will sneak in from the Gulf of California. On the western margin of the field guide area, the Sierra Nevada receives more than 50 inches of precipitation in an average year, mostly during the winter and early spring. The Sierra Nevada forces clouds to drop most of their moisture west of the crest of the range, creating a rain shadow in the areas to the east. The average annual precipitation in the Carson Desert is less than 5 inches.

Periods of above or below normal precipitation can last from 2 to 20 years. Because climatic records have only been kept for slightly more than 100 years, scientists are researching tree rings and evidence provided by stumps of mature trees found several hundred feet under the present level of Lake Tahoe to determine long-term variations in the regional climate. This is critical information to have because the metropolitan centers face continuous growth in this arid environment and depend upon variations in the limited water supply.

Winters in the mountains are cold, and summer daytime temperatures are warm to hot, except at the highest peaks. This region experiences one of the greatest ranges in diurnal temperatures in the nation. In the summer, the temperature in an area can vary more than 50 °F in a single day. In the Carson Desert, summers are warm (in the 90s) and winters are cold (but rarely below -5 °F).

Wind is common here. In *Roughing It*, Mark Twain commented on the "Washoe zephyrs" during a visit to Carson City in the early 1860s.

"...The "Washoe Zephyr" ... is a particularly scriptural wind, in that no man knoweth "whence it cometh." That is to say, where it origi-nates. It comes right over the mountains from the west, but when one crosses the ridge he does not find any of it on the other side! It is probably manufactured on the mountaintop for the occasion, and starts from there. It is a pretty regular wind, in the summertime. Its office hours are from two in the afternoon till two the next morn-ing; and anybody venturing abroad during those twelve hours needs to allow for the wind or he will bring up a mile or two to lee-ward of the point he was aiming at. ..."

The area's vegetation zones are largely determined by elevation and precipitation, but variations in soil type and chemistry (directly a result of the geology), exposure, and slope play an important role in local areas and will be noted along each of the routes.

GEOLOGY

The rocks in this region hold the rich mineral deposits that drew the immigrants here. Thus, geologic and human history are given the most attention in this volume. The rocks—their age and how they were formed—are described in detail in each log; however, brief overviews of some aspects of geology and of the Reno area geologic history are provided below.

THE THREE ROCK TYPES

Rocks are made of minerals. A mineral is a naturally occurring, inorganic, solid element or combination of elements with a definite chemical composition and a regular internal crystal structure. That is why minerals have certain definitive shapes and physical properties.

Rocks are classified into three major types depending on how they were formed. **Igneous rocks** are those that were previously molten, forming from magma (molten rock) from deep below the Earth's surface. Igneous rocks are given names on the basis of their composition and mode of formation. Most rising magma never reaches the surface, but cools slowly at depth forming masses of plutonic rocks such as stocks, batholiths, and dikes. Granite is an example of plutonic rock that contains relatively large amounts of silica and alkali metal elements (potassium, calcium, and sodium). Molten rock that reaches the surface through cracks in the Earth's crust produces volcanic rock. The various products of volcanic eruptions range from quiet lava flows to explosively erupted ash-flow tuffs and other pyroclastic rocks. Volcanoes form where these volcanic processes continue until large piles of volcanic rock collect. Basalt is a dark-colored volcanic rock type that contains relatively low silica and large amounts of iron and magnesium.

Sedimentary rocks are formed in two ways. Clastic sedimentary rock, such as sandstone, forms from accumulations of particles of preexisting rocks broken down and transported by the action of water, wind, ice, or gravity and deposited in new locations (in oceans, rivers, lakes, or desert basins). Nonclastic sedimentary rock is produced by chemically or biologically formed material precipitated out of certain bodies of water. Examples include some limestone and evaporite rocks such as gypsum. In time, the deposited rock particles and precipitates harden to form solid rock.

Sedimentary rocks may contain evidence of the life and environment that existed in the past—fossilized remains of plants and animals and traces of their existence such as burrows or tracks. Fossils, especially those of life forms that existed for geologically short periods, are especially useful in correlating rocks of the same age around the world.

Metamorphic rocks are preexisting rocks that have been changed by heat, pressure, and chemically active fluids, generally while in the solid state. Metamorphic rocks are physically different from the original rocks from which they were formed. They are commonly more dense and tough, and the original mineral grains have undergone changes in size or shape; entirely new minerals have also been formed. If high temperatures were involved, the former rocks may have been partially melted. Gneiss and schist are two common types of metamorphic rocks.

All three rocks types can be found in the Reno area, but igneous rocks have the greatest areal extent in this region.

GEOLOGIC STRUCTURES

Many geologic structures in the Reno area are described in the road logs that follow. Faults are common and well exposed in many places along the eastern front of the Sierra Nevada and in the mountain ranges to the east. The Basin and Range province is one of the most seismically active parts of the world and during some parts of geologic history was probably even more active. Faults may be classified into several types on the basis of steepness and the motion along them. High-angle normal and strike-slip faults are important structural features seen in this area.

PLATE TECTONICS

Early in the twentieth century, on the basis of physical and geologic correlations between continents, some

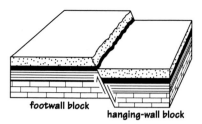

footwall block

hanging-wall block

NORMAL FAULT

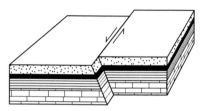

LEFT-LATERAL STRIKE-SLIP FAULT

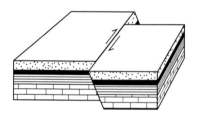

RIGHT-LATERAL STRIKE-SLIP FAULT

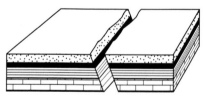

OBLIQUE-SLIP FAULT

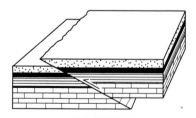

THRUST FAULT

Different kinds of faults.

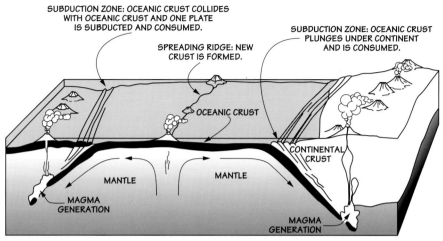

Simplified crustal block diagram showing plate tectonic processes at spreading ridges and subduction zones.

scientists proposed that the Earth's landmasses were mobile, sliding slowly about on the Earth's surface. This theory, called continental drift, was largely ignored in the United States until the 1960s, when new data were collected that convinced most scientists that the continents and the rocks of the ocean floor were indeed moving at rates of a few centimeters per year. Since that time many new concepts have evolved that include continental drift in an overall theory of crustal movement called plate tectonics.

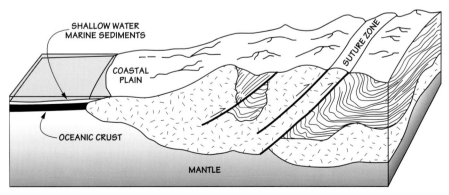

Simplified crustal block diagram showing a passive continental margin on the left and an eroded continent-continent collision on the right.

Major Divisions of Geologic Time

GEOLOGIC AGE				DOMINANT LIFE

CENOZOIC

Quaternary
- Holocene
  — 0.01 Ma
- Pleistocene
  — 1.6 Ma

Tertiary (T) — *Neogene*
- Pliocene
  — 5.3 Ma
- Miocene
  — 23.7 Ma

Tertiary (T) — *Paleogene*
- Oligocene
  — 36.6 Ma
- Eocene
  — 57.8 Ma
- Paleocene
  — 66 Ma

The several geologic eras were originally named Primary, Secondary, Tertiary, and Quaternary. The first two names are no longer used; Tertiary and Quaternary have been retained but used as period designations.

MESOZOIC

- Cretaceous (K)

Derived from Latin word for chalk (creta) and first applied to extensive deposits that form white cliffs along the English Channel.

  — 138 Ma
- Jurassic (J)

Named for the Jura Mountains, located between France and Switzerland, where rocks of this age were first studied.

  — 205 Ma
- Triassic (Ŧ)

Taken from word "trias" in recognition of the threefold character of these rocks in Europe.

  — 250 Ma

PALEOZOIC

- Permian (P)

Named after the ancient Kingdom of Permia in Russia, where these rocks were first studied.

  — 290 Ma
- Pennsylvanian (ℙ)

Named after the State of Pennsylvania where these rocks have produced much coal.

  — 330 Ma
- Mississippian (M)

Named for the Mississippi River valley where these rocks are well exposed.

  — 355 Ma
- Devonian (D)

Named after Devonshire, England, where these rocks were first studied.

  — 405Ma
- Silurian (S)
  — 435 Ma
- Ordovician (O)

Named after Celtic tribes, the Silures and Ordovices, that lived in Wales during the Roman Conquest.

  — 510 Ma
- Cambrian (Ꞓ)

Taken from Roman name for Wales (Cambria) where rocks containing the earliest evidence of complex forms of life were first studied.

  — 570 Ma

PRECAMBRIAN (pꞒ)

- Proterozoic (ℙ)

The time between the birth of the planet and the appearance of complex forms of life. More than 80 percent of the Earth's estimated 4$^1/_2$ billion years is Precambrian.

  — 2500 Ma
- Archean (A)
  — 4550 Ma

Ma = Mega-annum = million years

New oceanic crust is generated by magma emplaced into the sea floor at spreading ridges. Carpets of this oceanic crust move slowly away from the spreading ridges, possibly impelled by convection cells in the mantle in a configuration much like conveyor belts. As new crust forms at spreading ridges, it is consumed in areas called subduction zones, many of which are at the margins of continents. Downward moving (subducted) oceanic crust moves into the mantle at these subduction zones; magma produced by this process rises through the continental crust to become plutonic or volcanic rocks. This process is taking place today in the Cascade Range.

Margins between oceanic and continental crust are not always subduction zones; they may be areas of long-term sediment accumulation. In some areas, continental masses have been pushed together by plate movements. During recent geologic time, for example, India has been in collision with Asia, producing the massive Himalaya Mountains as a result of crustal buckling. Continental masses have collided many times throughout the Earth's history, and this is one of the principal ways that large continents are produced from smaller continental fragments.

Plate tectonic movements are also responsible for the separation of continents along intercontinental rifts, where the land is pulled apart because of the development of a new spreading zone. The East African rift system is a modern example of such a spreading zone.

GEOLOGIC HISTORY

Direct evidence about the geologic history of the Reno area is limited to relatively young rocks—Mesozoic and Cenozoic. Precambrian and Paleozoic rocks are not exposed. During the Paleozoic Era, the Reno area was a deep-water marine environment, while much of eastern Nevada was at the margin of the North American continent. The rocks that were deposited here on that quiescent continental margin are believed to have been later pushed eastward into central and eastern Nevada during the late Paleozoic and Mesozoic.

The Mesozoic Era, the age of the dinosaurs, was marked in west-central Nevada by a change from marine to continental sedimentary deposition. The western margin of the North American continent lay just west of the present Nevada-California border. This is the last time that central Nevada lay under the ocean.

The Mesozoic was also a time of significant regional change in the configuration of the Earth's crust. Beginning in the early Mesozoic, easterly moving rocks of the Pacific oceanic crust began to descend beneath the westerly moving North American continent along a subduction zone. Magma was produced at depth along this subduction zone resulting in outpourings of volcanic rocks of Triassic and Jurassic age that can be seen in the Reno area today as remnants in roof pendants surrounded by the granitic rocks of the Cretaceous Sierra Nevada batholith.

Continued magmatic activity in the Cretaceous Period produced the granitic rocks of the main intrusive (plutonic) igneous mass of the Sierra Nevada. The Sierra Nevada batholith represents the roots of a volcanic arc that was built on the continental margin in late Mesozoic time. The volcanic rocks that were once above this batholith have eroded away and the sediments derived from them were deposited to the west during the latest Cretaceous and early Tertiary.

Rocks of Mesozoic age in the Reno area consist of early to middle Mesozoic volcanic rocks and marine shale, limestone, and conglomerate that now are found in roof pendants in Cretaceous granitic plutons. These pendants and plutons make up the basement to the extensive Tertiary rocks that overlie them in the mountain ranges. Much of the Carson Range between Reno and Lake Tahoe is made up of granite, with pendants of the older Mesozoic rocks showing up in certain areas, such as Peavine Peak north of Reno, in the hills around Carson City, north of Washoe Lake, and near Genoa and Spooner Summit in the southern Carson Range.

During the Cenozoic Era, the Reno area underwent a second major change in the style of geologic movement. During the early part of this era, much of the western United States was probably a high plateau. As the Pacific oceanic crust continued to push under the west coast of North America, volcanism continued on a grand scale in most of Nevada. From Oligocene through early Miocene time enormous amounts of volcanic material were erupted as a result of this continued subduction. The older part of this sequence consists of large volume ash-flow sheets that were erupted from numerous calderas and spread over the eroded Mesozoic landscape. Above these rocks, we find mainly andesitic lavas. The andesites were erupted from numerous composite volcanoes similar to those of the Cascade Range of Washington and Oregon. During the last quarter of the Cenozoic, a change from subduction to strike-slip faulting at the continental margin resulted in the end of subduction-related volcanism, and in regional extension in the area we now call the Basin and Range. The area was, and continues to be literally pulled apart by these forces. The rocks have been tilted and broken by normal faults during this deformation.

During the latter part of the Cenozoic Era, extensional forces produced the mountain ranges and intervening valleys that are characteristic of the Basin and Range province. Nearly all mountain ranges in Nevada are bounded by at least one fault, and many of these faults are considered to be capable of producing major earthquakes.

Volcanic activity occurred along with the faulting during this time as magma rose from depth along vents and fissures that developed in the thinned crust. Large portions of the Reno area are covered with layer upon layer of volcanic rock, and the faults bounding the ranges are still active and visible. Lake Tahoe was formed by these processes of faulting and volcanism and modified, more recently, by glacial processes during the Pleistocene Epoch.

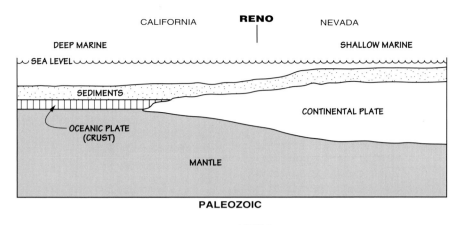

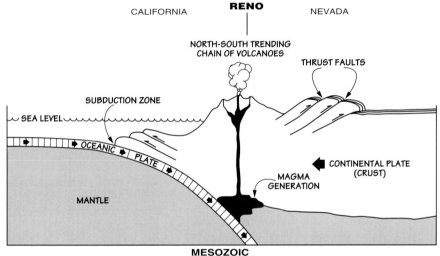

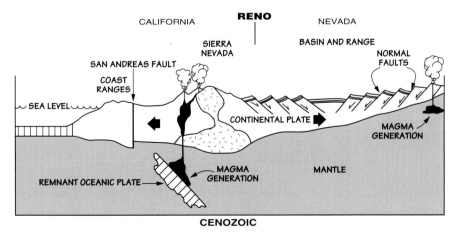

Cross sections from the Pacific Ocean through the present-day site of Reno showing geologic processes at work about 500 million years ago (Paleozoic Era), about 100 million years ago (Mesozoic Era), and about 10 million years ago (Cenozoic Era).

15

Cultural History

This area was inhabited by American Indians since, at least, the last glacial period when the weather was much wetter and cooler than now. Archeological evidence of the Desert Culture determined to be about 9,000 years old has been found. Petroglyphs have been found at many sites throughout the entire region. Symbols, hauntingly similar throughout the eastern Sierra Nevada, can be found scratched into rock varnish along the bases of lava flows or in the tufa deposits found high above present lake levels in basins once occupied by pluvial Lake Lahontan. Evidence strongly suggests that the modern Paiutes have been here for about 1,500 years, but their traditional beliefs say the Creator put them here at the beginning of time.

Several early explorers passed through this area in the mid-19th century in prelude to the immigrants who forged their routes to Oregon and California just a few years later. Many of these routes enter this area from

Petroglyphs located west of Winnemucca (dry) Lake. See page 33 for a color photo of other petroglyphs.

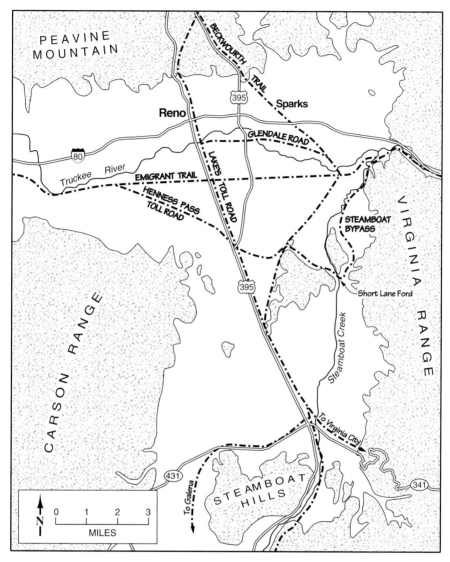

Trails of the early explorers and immigrants in the Truckee Meadows area.

the Humboldt River near Winnemucca. From Wadsworth, routes were established south to Silver Springs and then west to Carson City, or straight west through the Truckee River canyon to the Truckee Meadows (Reno-Sparks) and, from there, west or southwest over the Sierra Nevada to California.

John Frémont, Jim Beckwourth, Peter Lassen, Kit Carson, and Jedediah Smith were some of the more famous men to first explore this region.

Many families followed the routes they established and their diaries and official travel records have been published for the enlightenment of future generations.

In the early 1860s, Mark Twain crossed the Forty Mile Desert (east of Wadsworth) on his way to Virginia City and wrote the following account in *Roughing It:* "On the nineteenth day we crossed the Great American Desert—forty memorable miles of bottomless sand, into which the coach wheels sunk from six inches to a foot. We worked our passage most of the way across. That is to say, we got out and walked. It was a dreary pull and a long and thirsty one, for we had no water. From one extremity of this desert to the other, the road was white with the bones of oxen and horses. It would hardly be an exaggeration to say that we could have walked the forty miles and set out feet on a bone at every step! The desert was a prodigious graveyard. And the log chains, wagon tires, and rotting wrecks of vehicles were almost as thick as the bones. I think we saw log chains enough rusting there in the desert to reach across any state in the Union. Do not these relics suggest something of an idea of the fearful suffering and privation the early emigrants to California endured?"

People gave up everything they had back East for the promise of a new start and possible instant wealth in the California gold fields (gold was discovered in 1848 at Sutter's Mill near Coloma). In 1859 silver and gold were discovered in the Virginia Range—the Comstock Lode—and the "rush to Washoe" was on. This event, above all others, heralded the opening up of the West, the advent of the continental railroad, and Nevada's statehood. Much of the history of this era is described in Trip B.

TRIP A—RENO TO STEAMBOAT HOT SPRINGS

This trip begins at the University of Nevada, Reno (UNR) and continues south through Reno to Steamboat Hot Springs. The route traverses fan deposits of Peavine Mountain, crosses the Truckee River and its floodplain, continues over and along recent faults in glacial outwash reflecting the active seismic zone along the eastern boundary of the Carson Range, crosses the Moana geothermal area, and ends at the Steamboat Hot Springs geothermal area. At the end of this trip, you may continue on with Trip B or Trip C. The total distance of this trip is 12 miles.

0.0 Begin at the main entrance of UNR at Ninth and Center Streets. The columns of the stone gates at this entrance are dark gray granitic rock from a quarry on the west side of Washoe Valley. The lower

University of Nevada, Reno campus entrance.

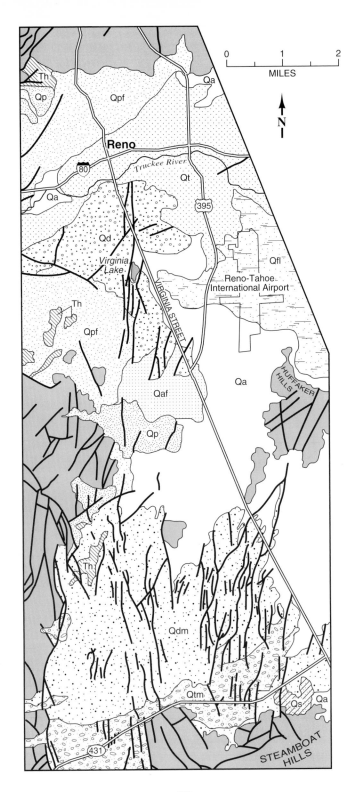

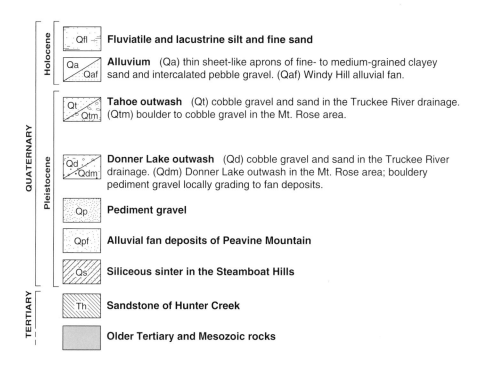

Qfl	Fluviatile and lacustrine silt and fine sand	Holocene
Qa / Qaf	**Alluvium** (Qa) thin sheet-like aprons of fine- to medium-grained clayey sand and intercalated pebble gravel. (Qaf) Windy Hill alluvial fan.	

Geology of the Reno area along U.S. 395 (Virginia Street) from the University of Nevada, Reno campus to Steamboat Hot Springs (Bingler, 1975).

Qfl Fluviatile and lacustrine silt and fine sand

Qa Qaf **Alluvium** (Qa) thin sheet-like aprons of fine- to medium-grained clayey sand and intercalated pebble gravel. (Qaf) Windy Hill alluvial fan.

Qt Qtm **Tahoe outwash** (Qt) cobble gravel and sand in the Truckee River drainage. (Qtm) boulder to cobble gravel in the Mt. Rose area.

Qd Qdm **Donner Lake outwash** (Qd) cobble gravel and sand in the Truckee River drainage. (Qdm) Donner Lake outwash in the Mt. Rose area; bouldery pediment gravel locally grading to fan deposits.

Qp **Pediment gravel**

Qpf **Alluvial fan deposits of Peavine Mountain**

Qs **Siliceous sinter in the Steamboat Hills**

Th **Sandstone of Hunter Creek**

Older Tertiary and Mesozoic rocks

QUATERNARY — Pleistocene — TERTIARY

course of block in the wall is a light gray andesite from a quarry site about 3 miles north of the University, and the upper course is reddish brown sandstone quarried at a site now occupied by the prison in Carson City. No building stone quarries are active in Reno today. UNR is built on partially cemented Quaternary alluvial fan deposits of Peavine Mountain, on the northwest margin on Reno. This fan material mantles the altered bedrock of northern Reno. (*Note:* Earth science facilities on the UNR campus that are well worth the visit are the Seismological Lab in the Laxalt Mineral Engineering Building, the William M. Keck Museum in the Mackay Mines Building, and the Information and Publication Sales offices of NBMG in the Scrugham Engineering-Mines Building.)

Set your odometer to 0.0 and turn right onto Ninth Street. Proceed one block.

0.1 **Turn left onto Virginia Street**. Cross over Interstate 80 (I-80). The low-gradient surface extending south from here marks the northern margin of the glacial outwash floodplain deposited by the Truckee River. This outwash deposit widens toward the east in the Truckee Meadows.

21

Roadcuts to the right along I-80 expose unconsolidated and interbedded glacial cobble gravel and coarse sand overlain by a veneer of Peavine Mountain fan deposits approximately 10 feet thick. These fan deposits thin rapidly to a feather edge south of I-80.

0.6 Passing under the Reno Arch. This is the third such structure at this site. The first arch was built across Virginia Street in October 1926, and read "The Transcontinental Highway Exposition—Reno" to signify the completion of the Lincoln and Victory Highways. In March 1929, the current slogan, "Reno—The Biggest Little City in the World" was hung on that arch after a contest was held to select a new slogan for Reno. That arch now stands on Lake Street in front of the William F. Harrah National Automobile Museum. A second arch was completed and dedicated on New Year's Eve 1963, and the present arch replaced that arch in August 1987.

Reno arch as it looks today.

RENO'S EARLY DAYS

The emigrant trail to California followed the Truckee River westward through the Truckee Meadows. Several routes crossed the valley. In 1859, C.W. Fuller established a toll ferry and later a bridge on the Truckee River at the site of the present Lake Street bridge two blocks east of Virginia Street. In 1861, Fuller sold his enterprise to Myron C. Lake and the site became known as Lake's Crossing. Lake continued to build toll roads, hotels, and related structures to accommodate the increasing numbers of travelers and their freight, much of which was related to the discovery of the Comstock Lode in Virginia City in 1859 (see Trip B). He became a wealthy man.

As the Central Pacific (now the Southern Pacific) Railroad advanced its line eastward over the Sierra Nevada, plans were made to establish a town at the site of Lake's Crossing. Lake deeded land to the railroad and on May 9, 1868 a land auction was held at the new railroad station. The first train arrived on June 18. The new town had several unofficial names before an

Lake's house and Courthouse (1880s). The original site of Lake's Crossing.

Virginia Street and the Reno Arch in the late 1950s.

official of the railroad named the town after Major General Jesse Lee Reno, a Union officer who was killed in action in 1862. In those times of post-Civil War patriotism it was customary to name places after war heroes.

The Virginia and Truckee Railroad (V & T) linked Reno to Virginia City in 1872, boosting Reno's prosperity as a distribution and trading point on the railway system.

In 1900, people began to flock to Reno for an entirely different reason— Nevada's 6-week divorce law, which had been in effect since 1861. Gambling was first licensed in Nevada in 1879, outlawed in 1910, and in successive years repeatedly licensed and outlawed until it was finally legalized in 1931.

0.8 Crossing the Truckee River. This perennial stream drains Lake Tahoe basin and valleys to the west and flows eastward to end in Pyramid Lake, a total of about 100 miles. "Truckee" is a common word in this area and honors Chief Truckee of the Paiute Nation. It means "all right" or "very well." (Refer to page 143 for more detailed information on the geology of the Truckee Meadows and the Truckee River.)

Immediately after crossing the river, the surface rising ahead is composed of older (estimated to be older than 200,000 years) bouldery glacial outwash.

Truckee River near downtown Reno, 1995.

24

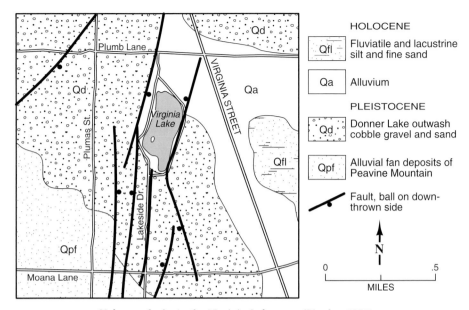

Holocene faults in the Virginia Lake area (Bingler, 1975).

1.1 Crossing California Street.

1.9 **Turn right onto Mount Rose Street** and proceed up the glacial out-wash floodplain which has probably been tilted by Quaternary fault-ing and warping.

2.1 **Turn left onto Lakeside Drive.** For the next few blocks Lakeside Drive parallels an inferred fault that separates Pleistocene glacial outwash on the right (upthrown block) from Holocene alluvium on the left (downthrown block).

2.4 Cross Plumb Lane. Lakeside Drive continues to parallel the fault that now becomes more defined by the bluff of glacial outwash on the right.

2.5 **Keep right** at the "Y" intersection on Lakeside Drive. Virginia Lake occupies a small, natural fault-bounded depression, or graben, mod-ified by man on the north end to form a closed basin.

2.6 After crossing Wildrose Drive, look to the right at the upthrown side of the fault with about 20 feet of displacement.

*Upthrown Holocene fault block that parallels the west side of
Lakeside Drive at Wildrose Drive.*

Across the lake to the left, the eastern shore, also composed of outwash material, is defined by another fault which is down-dropped on the lake (west) side. (See Introduction for an explanation of fault terms.)

Continue along the west side of the lake.

2.9 Proceed up a slight slope on Lakeside Drive. Several branching faults intersect here.

3.4 Moana Lane intersection. Ahead and to the left are elongate, low-lying, fault-bounded (down-to-the-west faults) hills of glacial outwash. There are marshy areas on both sides of Lakeside Drive beyond the intersection. These points where the water table intersects the ground surface are probably controlled by the fault on the left at 11:00. Notice the scarp below the white house.

Turn left onto Moana Lane. Cross a fault escarpment and climb a hill of glacial outwash. Cross the summit (where the shopping center ends to the right) and proceed down the slope which has been tilted due to faulting and dissected by streams.

This stretch of west Moana Lane is the approximate center of a 4- to 5-square-mile area that produces water ranging from 160 to 205 °F from wells that are 100 to 300 feet deep in alluvium and Tertiary sedimentary rocks. The hot water has been used for commercial and residential heating for over 60 years. The Moana Hot Springs (not presently flowing, but originally located near here) are the locus of this geothermal anomaly, which parallels the base of the Carson Range to the west. Several faults in this area cut glacial deposits.

The hot wells are located along a north-south-striking alignment, presumably a fault. Water in these wells stands higher than the local water table. The surrounding wells generally have lower temperatures. The hot waters have probably diffused laterally after

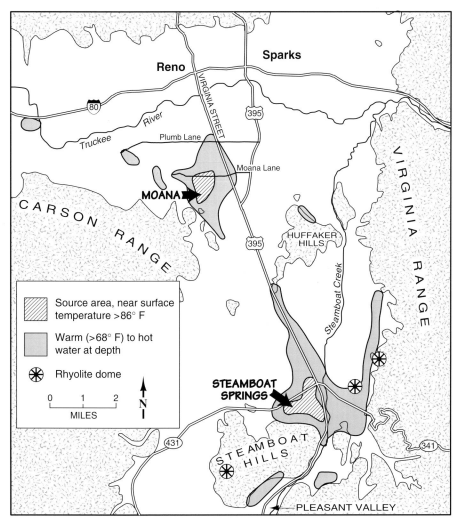

Locations of the Moana and Steamboat Hot Springs geothermal areas and Pleistocene rhyolite domes in the Truckee Meadows (modified from Bateman and Scheibach, 1975).

Moana Springs bath house, circa 1900.

rising along one or more faults. The waters are contained above by an impermeable clay zone. Hot water is generally not found above this clay zone and many cold water wells are drilled throughout this area.

3.8 To the right, the Moana municipal pool is heated by geothermal water from a 500-foot well.

4.0 Turn right (south) onto Virginia Street. This is the approximate boundary between the glacial outwash on the right and sediments deposited in a large floodplain-swamp-lake complex. Urban development has obliterated the surface expression of these deposits.

4.2 The Junction House historical marker is on the left in front of the Clarion Casino/Hotel. This was a converging point for many of Nevada's earliest emigrant trails and toll roads (see map on page 17. By 1853, the first permanent settlement in the Truckee Meadows was established here and was known as Junction House (later called Anderson's). From this point, travelers proceeded on to Washoe City, Virginia City, Oregon, and the Henness Pass route to California.

4.3 Peckham Lane intersection. Peckham Lane closely follows the emigrant route through the eastern Truckee Meadows.

4.7 Kietzke Lane intersection.

5.1 McCarran Blvd. intersection.

5.8 Del Monte Lane intersection. **Get in the left lane** in preparation for the turn at the next intersection.

6.6 Turn left onto Longley Lane for a side trip to Huffaker Park.

6.9 Turn right onto Huffaker Lane.

7.3 Turn right onto Offenhauser Drive. Park across from Huffaker Park. The trail climbing the hill is easily visible across the creek (east of the restrooms). There is a walking tour about 0.5 mile in length. Walk to the gazebo at the top of the hill for a great view of the southern Truckee Meadows. **Take your book along** to read about formation of the present landforms.

The Huffaker Hills are composed of Miocene volcanic flows and domes, containing large black crystals of hornblende and biotite.

From right (north) to left (south) on the western skyline are Peavine Peak (elev. 8,266 feet), and Mount Rose (elev. 10,776 feet), and Slide Mountain (elev. 9,698 feet) in the Carson Range.

Looking west at the Carson Range from the Huffaker Park gazebo. Note the fault trace that trends north-south along the base of the Carson Range at the top of the massive alluvial fan complex. This fan complex is highly faulted—cut by a plexus of north-trending faults.

Age			Formation	Description
QUATERNARY	Holocene		Alluvium (recent)	Gravel, sand, and silt
			.010 Ma (10,000 years)	
	Pleistocene		Glacial outwash and alluvial fan deposits	Sand and gravel
			Older alluvium	Gravel and sand
			McClellan Peak Basalt (1.5 Ma)	Black to dark gray basalt flow and cinders with green olivine phenocrysts
			unconformity	
	Pliocene		Steamboat Hills Rhyolite domes (~1 Ma)	Rhyolite and pumiceous glass, perlite, minor obsidian and air-fall tuff and waterlaid tuff
			Basaltic andesite of Steamboat Hills (2.5 Ma)	Dark gray basaltic andesite flows with phenocrysts of plagioclase and olivine
			unconformity	
TERTIARY	Miocene		Lousetown Formation (7-10 Ma)	Flows of dark gray to black platy basaltic andesite and olivine basalt. Some intrusives. Weathered surfaces are dark brown.
			unconformity	
			Sandstone of Hunter Creek (6-10 Ma)	Sandstone, shale, tuff, and diatomite
			Washington Hill Rhyolite (11 Ma)	Rhyolite and pumiceous glass, perlite, minor obsidian and air-fall and water-laid tuff
			Kate Peak Formation and related rocks (12-16 Ma)	Porphyritic dacite and rhyodacite flows, domes, pyroclastic flows, lahars, plugs dikes, and related rocks. Phenocrysts of sodic plagioclase, pyroxene, hornblende, and biotite in a light-colored matrix. Flow rocks are somewhat porous, weather spheroidally, and turn brown on the surface.
			local unconformity	
			Alta Formation (17-20 Ma)	Pyroxene adesite flows and related rocks. Phenocrysts of plagioclase and dark minerals in a fine-grained matrix. Flow rocks medium to dark gray on fresh surfaces, weathering to brown.
		Oligocene	*regional unconformity*	
			Silicic ash flow tuffs, locally present	Rhyolitic to dacitic ash flow tuff, as erosional remnants below Alta Formation.
			major regional unconformity	
CRETACEOUS			Granodiorite (Sierra Nevada)	Gray hornblende-biotite granodiorite
JURASSIC / TRIASSIC			Peavine sequence	Gray to gray-green metamorphosed volcanic and sedimentary rocks (rhyolite flows and pyroclastics; dacite and andesite flows; sandstone and conglomerate containing abundant volcanic detritus.
			Gardnerville Formation	Gray marble, siltstone, and volcaniclastic rocks

Stratigraphic column for the Reno-Virginia City-Carson City area.

Although the Carson Range is considered part of the Sierra Nevada because it is composed of the same rock types, it is structurally similar to the Basin and Range physiographic province because it is bounded by basin-and-range-type faults. About 25 million years ago, major volcanic eruptions began in this area. Beginning about 13 million years ago, a second major pulse of volcanism occurred in the area (including the area around Lake Tahoe). The Earth's crust was beginning to stretch apart (extend) in Nevada. This extension was accompanied by faulting and rotation of the rocks. The nearby mountains were uplifted. Molten lava intruded numerous faults in the Carson Range, Virginia Range, Peavine Peak, and Steamboat Hills, producing hydrothermal systems (similar to the ones presently at Steamboat Hot Springs) that deposited the precious metals later mined in these areas.

The current uplift of the Carson Range began about 5 million years ago or less. Faulting, uplift and volcanism around Lake Tahoe have progressed together from late Tertiary (Miocene-Pliocene) through Quaternary time.

The Truckee Meadows valley was formed when the mountains on both sides were uplifted relative to the down-dropped valley floor; the rocks warped and broke away from each other along fault zones, like those you have just seen in the Virginia Lake and Moana Lane areas.

The broad bowl on the side of Mount Rose and its high U-shaped valleys were scoured out by glaciers during the Pleistocene Epoch. Mount Rose appears darker than the other peaks in the Carson Range because it is capped with a layer of darker Miocene volcanic rocks. Note the huge, sloping, alluvial fan extending eastward from the Carson Range. The sediments were deposited by streams draining glaciers on Mount Rose. The slope has been accentuated by the continued downward tilting of the eastern margin of the Truckee Meadows. (Refer to page 105 for more detailed information on the Sierra Nevada frontal fault zone along the eastern border of the Carson Range in this area.)

Return to your vehicle and continue south on Offenhauser Drive to Portman. **Turn right onto Portman.**

7.8 Turn left onto Patriot Blvd.

8.0 Turn left onto U.S. 395 (South Virginia Street).

8.2 Cross under the freeway.

9.0 Foothill Road intersection.

10.5 Zolezzi Lane intersection. Note the quarry operations at the base of the Virginia Range to the left. The Pleistocene rhyolite domes are

Rilite Aggregate quarry at the base of the Virginia Range.

being quarried for lightweight aggregate for use in concrete, roadbase material, and asphalt pavement. (Refer to map on page 27)

The Steamboat Hills are ahead at 1:00.

11.3 Cross under the freeway.

11.8 Intersection of U.S. 395 (south to Carson City), State Route 341 (east to Virginia City), and State Route 431 (west to Lake Tahoe via Mount Rose).

Note: A description of the Steamboat Hot Springs geothermal area is given at the end of Trip B (see page 98).

End of Trip A.

Turn left onto State Route 341 to begin Trip B

or

Turn right onto State Route 431 to begin Trip C.

Petroglyphs located in Lagomarsino Canyon north of Virginia City.

Big sagebrush (Artemisia tridentata).

33

Mormon tea (Ephedra sp.).

Desert peach in bloom (Prunus andersonii).

34

Aerial view looking south over Virginia City.

View of Sugarloaf looking southeast down Sixmile Canyon.

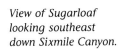

Aerial view of the Mount Rose fan complex looking west at the Carson Range.

Aerial view of Lake Tahoe.

Trees killed by bark beetles in the Lake Tahoe basin.

Close-up of beetle damage to a Jeffrey pine.

Terri Garside photo.

Looking west, the vertical escarpment of the Sierra Nevada frontal fault zone (on the left) rises above the floor of the Carson Valley. Lake Tahoe is in the background.

Aerial view of Lake Tahoe looking west. Spooner Lake is in the foreground.

View looking southeast at the scenic view stop at mile 14.6 on I-80 (see page 150).

Horizontal lines in black basalt mark strandlines (above) and layers of light-colored lake sediment (below) at the base of the Truckee Range (see page 167).

Neal Brecheisen photos.

Indian ricegrass (Oryzopsis hymenoides).

Tom Purkey photo.

The Pyramid on Pyramid Lake at sunset.

40

TRIP B—VIRGINIA CITY-CARSON CITY-WASHOE VALLEY-STEAMBOAT HOT SPRINGS

On this trip, you will climb up the new Geiger Grade to Virginia City, built on the famous Comstock Lode. Along the way the origin of the colorful rocks and changes in vegetation will be explained. Industrial and precious metal mineral deposits will be described, as well as many historical sites as you pass through Virginia City, Gold Hill, Silver City, Carson City, and Washoe Valley. In the last half of the 19th century, this entire area was bound by a common tie: recovering the rich ore of the Comstock mines. You'll trace the route of the famous Virginia & Truckee (V & T) Railroad, pass ruins of ore and lumber mills, and cross over the recent debris flows of Slide Mountain in Washoe Valley. The trip ends at Steamboat Hot Springs on the south end of the Truckee Meadows. These springs have the longest and most complex geologic history of any active geothermal system in the world. On this trip you'll see great examples of one of Nevada's state trees (singleleaf pinyon), the state flower (big sagebrush), and possibly, the state bird (mountain bluebird). It was from this area, the Comstock Lode, that Nevada's state slogan, "Battle Born," was derived. The rich mineral wealth of this area was needed to finance the Civil War, thus Nevada was ushered into statehood. The length of this trip is about 50 miles. Gas stations and restaurants abound.

0.0   Begin this trip at the intersection of U.S. 395 and State Routes 431 (to Lake Tahoe) and 341 (to Virginia City). **Set your odometer to 0.0 as you turn left onto State Route 341** (the Geiger Grade) to Virginia City.

       Caution: This is a narrow, winding route used by many motorists who are here to sightsee and are not familiar with the road. Please use extra caution when turning off the road and when resuming travel. Use the marked turnouts if anyone behind you wants to pass.

       To the left at 10:00 is a view of a rhyolite dome being mined for lightweight aggregate.

0.6   Toll Road on the right. This is the route of the original Geiger-Tilton Toll Road built to connect Reno and Virginia City. The new road parallels the original route in many places on the way to the top of the Virginia Range.

1.5   Start ascending the Virginia Range. Although the large light-colored boulders just ahead to the left of the road look out of place, they have

41

eroded from a small up-faulted block of Sierra Nevada granodiorite (look up the hill to the left of the water tank at the bouldery outcrop, weathered brown).

THE VIRGINIA RANGE

The Virginia Range is composed of a thick section (as thick as 11,000 feet) of Tertiary volcanic rocks consisting mainly of ash-flow tuff, rhyolite, andesite, basalt, and mud-flow breccia (lahar). Related intrusive igneous rocks include granodiorite dikes and stocks. Unconformities are common. Some sedimentary lacustrine (lake) deposits are interspersed with the volcanic rocks. These Tertiary volcanic and sedimentary rocks unconformably overlie metamorphosed Jurassic(?) sedimentary and volcanic rocks and Cretaceous granitic rocks. See the stratigraphic section on page 30.

Structurally, the range consists of west-tilted blocks bounded by normal (dip-slip), northeast- to northwest-trending faults that dip moderately or steeply to the east, and are step-faulted down to the east. Repeated tilting and warping, accompanied by block faulting, took place from Miocene through Quaternary time along axes that trend northeast to northwest. Most of this deformation occurred in the last 7 million years. The major period of mineralization associated with the Comstock Lode occurred 14 to 12 million years ago.

The range is bounded on the north by the Truckee River (which occupies the Olinghouse fault zone) and on the south by the Carson River and the Carson lineament (fault zone).

Just above the valley floor, which is dominated by sagebrush, pinyon-juniper woodland populates the hills. The pinyon-juniper woodland of the Great Basin covers middle to low slopes of the ranges at elevations of 5,000 to 8,000 feet, where the mean annual precipitation is between 12 to 18 inches. Species making up this Virginia Range woodland consist of singleleaf pinyon, Utah juniper , and western juniper. Utah juniper is more drought resistant than pinyon, and western juniper needs even less water than the Utah juniper.

Singleleaf pinyon

Big sagebrush dominates the understory of the woodland and usually occurs both lower and higher on the mountain slopes than pinyon and juniper. Other shrubs including Mormon tea (ephedra), desert peach, bitterbrush, and rabbitbrush share this terrain. Wildflowers abound in April and May, particularly after a wet winter. See color photos of desert peach, Mormon tea, and big sagebrush on pages 33 and 34.

Thermal inversions are common in the Truckee Meadows and in many other valleys in the Great Basin, especially during the winter and early spring, and the pinyon-juniper woodland rarely extends below the inversion layer in these valleys. During inversions, the woodlands are warmer than

42

Pinyon-juniper woodland (Pinus monophylla, Juniperus osteosperma).

the slopes below as well as the slopes above them. Air temperatures in the valley bottoms can be as much as 15° lower than in the woodlands.

2.8 Carefully turn off to the right.

This was the site of a pit where clay was mined mainly during the 1940s and 1950s to make bricks. Most of the pit is in altered andesite. The full mining area can be seen if you look back from a point along the road about 0.5 mile ahead.

For the next several miles up the Geiger Grade, hydrothermally altered Miocene rocks form white to pale brown bleached patches on the slopes ahead. The altered area is several square miles in extent and is controlled by numerous fracture zones with roughly north-south and east-west orientations. Hydrothermal breccia is common along these fracture zones. The alteration is both older and younger than the mineralizing event that formed the Comstock Lode ores. A buried porphyry copper system, perhaps hosting high-level gold deposits, may underlie this altered area but it is probably too deep to mine at present.

Hydrothermal acid sulfate alteration of rocks occurs when rocks are leached by fluids containing high concentrations of sulfuric acid. Sulfuric acid can be generated by different mechanisms in different

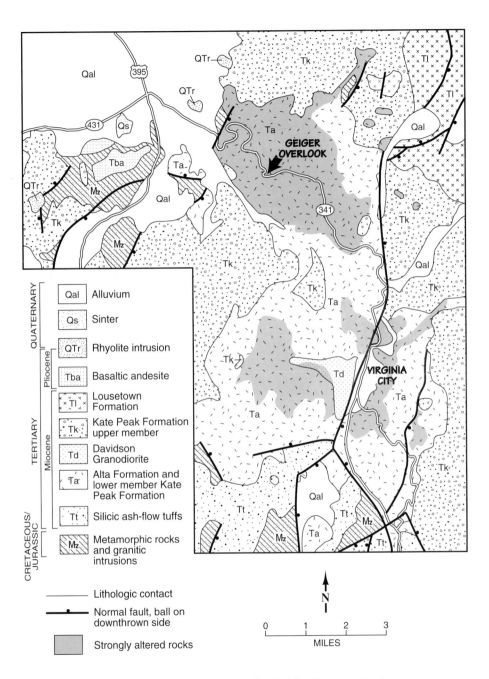

Geologic map of the Geiger Grade-Virginia City area showing
areas of altered rocks (after Hudson, 1987).

44

geologic environments. In the Virginia Range, the rock has been altered by (1) steam-heated waters, rich in sulfuric acid produced by oxidation of hydrogen sulfide from an underlying hydrothermal system, and by (2) hydrothermal fluids that are driven by the heat of a magma body. In this environment the magma produces high amounts of sulfur dioxide which combines with water to produce sulfuric acid and hydrogen sulfide. These plumes may also contain large amounts of hydrochloric acid. This type of alteration is usually controlled by the fractures in the rock, and zones of alteration (composed of different suites of minerals) occur outward from mineralized fractures.

Note how vegetation varies with soil type on the Geiger Grade in the Virginia Range. Pinyon grows on the darker, less altered andesite (left) and Jeffrey pine grows on the light, more altered volcanic rocks (right).

From this location, look at the hills ahead and note that the vegetation is distinctly different on the dark (less altered) rocks from that on the light-colored (more altered) volcanic rocks. (*Note:* Similar areas of acid sulfate alteration also occur in the Carson Range, in the hills north of Reno, at the north end of the Virginia Range, and on the flanks of Peavine Peak.)

Sagebrush, pinyon, and juniper have different requirements for moisture, soil chemistry, and soil pH than Jeffrey pine. Sagebrush needs a certain level of phosphorus in the soil, a soil pH of 6.5 to 7.5,

Artemisia tridentata

and can adapt to low precipitation and long periods of drought. Pinyon and juniper need about the same elements and more water than sagebrush. Soils derived from slightly altered andesite has a pH of 6.5 to 7.5, making it suitable for sagebrush and pinyon-juniper woodland.

Here, well-altered andesite has had most elements leached by acid, leaving behind mostly alumina and silica in clay minerals. The soil pH is less than 5.6 and can be very acid. Jeffrey pine can survive with reduced mineral content and increased acidity. Even in this arid climate, Jeffrey pine can exist on these sites because no other major species can grow here and compete for the water.

2.9 On either side of the road, note the brilliant red outcrops of ferricrete, or iron oxide-cemented alluvium. This is a deposit of pebbles and clay particles cemented by ferric iron oxides produced during weathering of pyrite-bearing, hydrothermally altered volcanic rocks.

Elsewhere along this route, the altered rock may be shades of gray or green. This indicates that the iron is in the reduced (ferrous) state.

3.4 The route passes through outcrops of unaltered volcanic breccia (lahars). The rock fragments and the matrix cementing them together have a similar mineral composition.

3.7 Note the conical rock outcrops to the left in the canyon and directly ahead. These are intrusive plugs and dikes of basalt and basaltic andesite dated at about 7.4 million years old. The columnar jointing in the intrusive rocks developed perpendicular to the cooler surfaces of the wallrock, such as in a volcanic neck or dike. Basaltic andesite is somewhat lighter colored than basalt, which is darker due to a higher content of dark minerals such as pyroxene, olivine, and magnetite. Plagioclase is usually the only feldspar, and quartz is very rare or absent.

Volcanic necks or dikes along the Geiger Grade.

46

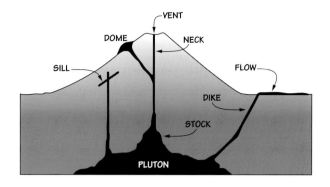

Generalized diagram of a composite volcano showing igneous rock terminology.

4.0 In the hills just ahead are excellent examples of occupancy by Jeffrey pine on altered volcanic sites that are too acidic for other species.

4.1 Passing/No parking zone on the right. Immediately to the left an outcrop displays tilted (by faulting) altered volcanic rocks overlain by relatively unaltered basaltic andesite.

4.7 Turn off to the right to scenic overlook.

The Geiger Grade overlook is a stop worth making. Walk out to the observation area and get a great view of the Truckee Meadows and Reno (the lights of Reno are spectacular at night), the Mount Rose glacial outwash fan complex, the Carson Range, the Steamboat Hills and Steamboat Hot Springs below, and Pleasant Valley beyond Steamboat Hills to the south (left). The rocks at the overlook are hydrothermally altered and brecciated andesite.

An outcrop displays tilted (by faulting) altered volcanic rocks overlain by relatively unaltered basaltic andesite.

Resume travel up the grade. There are more small stands of Jeffrey pine growing on altered andesite in the canyon to the right.

Wild mustangs in the Virginia Range.

A range fire burned the drainage area to the right in 1985 and again in 1995. If you haven't already spied a herd of wild mustangs, now is the time to be on the lookout. Several herds roam the Virginia Range all year long, and they are a beautiful sight. Sightings are more likely near Virginia City.

5.9 Look down in the canyon to the right to see the original Geiger-Tilton Toll Road.

6.3 Entering Storey County, named after Edward Faris Storey, captain of Company K (the Virginia Rifles) who was killed in the Pyramid Lake Indian War on June 2, 1860, shortly after moving to Virginia City.

7.4 **Turn off to the right**. Geiger-Tilton Toll Road Historical Marker.

The original road can be seen in the valley below. Davison M. Geiger and John H. Tilton completed this road in 1862, just a few years after the discovery of the Comstock Lode. It was over this road in 1869 that the locomotives for the V & T Railroad were hauled by oxen. The "Virginia" made it in three weeks, but the "Carson" had to be dismantled and hauled up in pieces.

7.7 The route traverses a flat mature upland which is an old erosion surface. The entrance to the Virginia City Highland neighborhood is on the left.

8.6 Carefully turn off to the right at the turnout.

The outcrop on the left side of the highway shows highly fractured altered andesite (tans and yellows) overlain by gray, less altered andesite. The pinyon-juniper woodland is particularly thick here, now that the route has left most of the area of altered rock.

"Pinyon" is the anglicized form of the Spanish "*piñon*," the edible seeds of desert conifers. The trees are, in Spanish, *pinos piñoneros*, or nut-bearing pines. Pine nuts were a staple food of early inhabitants of the Great Basin. They were served in soup and as a boiled or roasted mush. The nuts were stored in caches and, as winter progressed, used as the mainstay of their diet, because weather prevented great hunts for meat. Modern descendants of the aboriginal American Indians still supplement their diet with pinyon nuts, gathering them using time-honored methods passed from generation to generation.

The seed of the pinyon is large in relation the small size of the tree. The seed crops are unreliable: good crops occur only every 3 to 7 years and vary from one geographic region to another. Some scientists have postulated that poor crops are due to hard freezes in late spring which damage the new seed. It is this variance of seed crop that caused the early Americans to follow the harvest from place to place each fall. Because it takes 2 years for the seeds to mature, they were able to predict where the next year's harvest and celebration would take place. (Refer to M.M. Wheat and R.M. Lanner in the Bibliography for references explaining the Paiutes' entire process and important spiritual ritual involved in harvesting pine nuts.) Pinyon seeds have a moist and mild flavor. Recipe books are available for other tasty meal ideas using pine nuts.

9.3 Geiger Summit (elev. 6,789 feet). This is the southern limit of alteration zones in the Virginia Range. Note the yellow-green lichen covering the north face of the cliffs at 1:00.

The cliff-forming outcrops along the route to Virginia City are mainly various shades of gray andesite. The andesite takes on variations in color depending upon the mineralogic makeup of the various volcanic flows and whether the rock has been altered.

10.2 Carefully turn off to the right at the turnout.

The hills off to the left in the distance are the Flowery Range, composed mostly of volcanic rocks. The white layer at the base of the range is in an area known as the Chalk Hills. Rocks there are diatomite, shale, sandstone, conglomerate, tuff, mudstone, and siltstone. These sedimentary rocks contain fossil plant remains (mostly reedy plants) and an occasional fossil insect, amphibian, or small mammal (indicating a shallow lake and marsh environment). Refer to the publications by D.I. Axelrod in the Bibliography for more information on these fossil localities.

The flat tableland at 8:30 is underlain by late Miocene basalt.

11.1 Intersection with Lousetown Road on the left. Long Valley extends east and north from here. This was the original route—via Long Valley—for the Virginia and Truckee toll road which connected Lockwood, on the Truckee River, with Virginia City before the Geiger-Tilton Toll Road was completed. Louisa Town, a station on the original toll road, was located about 8 miles north of here in a scenic canyon with a flowing stream fed by springs.

11.7 Andesite dikes form resistant monoliths to the right just above the road. These intrude altered andesite flows that are exposed in the roadcuts ahead.

12.2 Straight ahead is Cedar Hill Canyon. More resistant dikes protrude from the hills on the right. There is a picturesque riparian area farther up the canyon.

12.3 Sevenmile Canyon is to the left of the road. Dumps of the Sierra Nevada mine can be seen at 10:00. This mine is on the north end of the Comstock Lode.

12.8 The Masonic Cemetery is on the left (several other cemeteries share this rise between Sevenmile and Sixmile Canyon), and the Cedar Hill pit is on the right.

12.9 Entering Virginia City (elev. 6,200 feet). This is a National Historic Landmark. It is against the law to remove any artifacts.

13.1 **Turn left into the parking/picnic area on the left. Stop here for a tour of Virginia City and the Comstock Lode.**

Resistant dikes of andesite stand out on the hillside above Cedar Hill Canyon.

Dumps of the Sierra Nevada mine on the north end of town. Note the large Jeffrey pines growing on the altered volcanic material comprising the dumps.

VIRGINIA CITY

Take time to see the historical sights. Most of the buildings you see date from 1876; they were built after the great fire of 1875 destroyed most of the town. Historical walking tour brochures can be obtained at several of the shops in the center of town. Interesting places to tour include: the cemeteries on the left; the shops, saloons, museums, the Marshall Mint mineral collection, and the Fourth Ward School on C Street; the Mackay, Savage, and Chollar mansions on D Street; "The Castle," the courthouse, Piper's Opera House, and other old meeting halls on B Street; and the churches and beautifully restored old homes around town. Ride the V & T Railroad. Open bus and horse-drawn carriage tours are offered throughout most of the year, and good food can be found in the many restaurants. Several grocery stores, an RV park, and a gas station operate here all year and Miner's Park (just ahead and to the left on Carson Street) offers a beautiful picnic area, and a public swimming pool (summers only). **Remember: "Stay out and stay alive" when venturing around abandoned mines.**

51

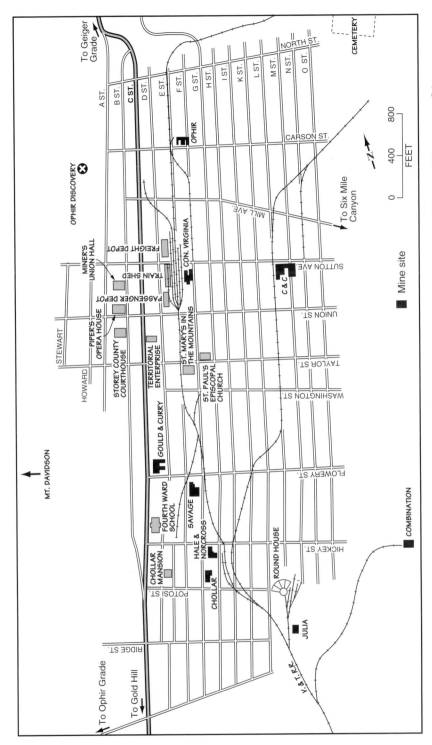

Map of Virginia City, showing historical sites and railroad routes. See color aerial photo of Virginia City on page 34.

From this rest area look south down C Street through Virginia City. Mount Davidson is on the right. It was originally called Sun Mountain but later changed to honor Donald Davidson, a representative of a British bank that helped finance mines on the Comstock. It is composed of granodiorite. The Comstock fault is defined by the break in slope just above the town and the line of pits along the fault marks the surface exposure of the Comstock Lode, which is mostly covered by alluvium and dumps.

From here, much of the north and middle parts of the mining district are visible. The Ophir pit is about 1,000 feet to the southwest and the Cedar Hill pit is about 1,500 feet to the north. Just over a mile to the south, where this trip will resume, is the Loring Cut. Numerous dumps are visible to the east (downhill from C Street) marking the shafts that explored the Lode at depth. To the southeast about 1,000 feet (near the swimming pool) is the Ophir Shaft, and about 2,000 feet to the south are dumps from the Consolidated Virginia Shaft. Sugarloaf, the monolith protruding from Sixmile Canyon to the east, is an andesitic volcanic neck (color photo on page 35).

Optional side trip to the original Ophir discovery site: Turn right on Carson Street. Proceed uphill for about three blocks to where the street makes an abrupt turn to the right. Stop. To the left (south) is the Virginia City pit where surface outcrops of the Comstock Lode were mined for several hundred feet downward in 1859-60, and again in the late 1920s. **Return to C Street.**

GEOLOGY OF THE COMSTOCK LODE

The Comstock Lode is a fault system that in many places contains rich silver and gold ore. It extends in a north-south direction along the eastern base of Mount Davidson from the Sierra Nevada mine on the north end of Virginia City to the Overman mine at the south end of the town of Gold Hill, a distance of about 3 miles. From 1859 to 1994, the total production from this district was over 190 million ounces of silver and 8 million ounces of gold.

The Comstock fault is almost vertical near the surface, then dips 35 to 40 degrees east, flattening slightly at depth. The Comstock Lode is a 9,000-foot-long stockwork zone of quartz and some calcite over 300 feet wide at the ground surface, narrowing to about 100 feet or less at depth. The rich orebodies within the fault zone are very irregular in shape. They rarely exceed 500 feet in vertical extent, 90 feet in mining width, and 750 feet in length.

The Comstock Lode is a precious metal hydrothermal system (similar in some ways to the modern hot springs at Steamboat Hot Springs at the end of this trip), preserved due to post-mineral faulting and limited erosion.

The ore was formed 12 to 14 million years ago during tectonic (mountain-building) and volcanic activity in this area. Rich in precious elements,

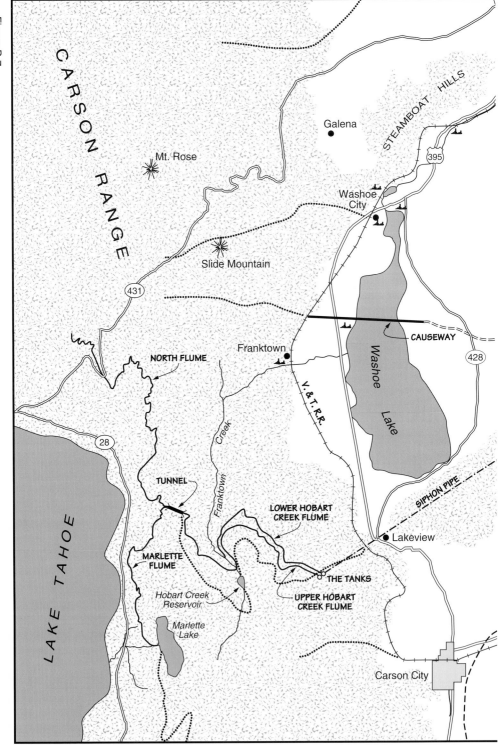

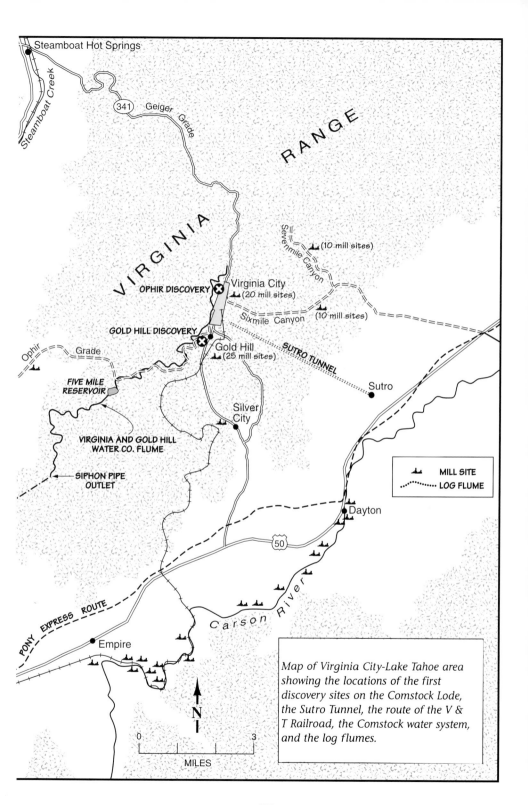

Map of Virginia City-Lake Tahoe area showing the locations of the first discovery sites on the Comstock Lode, the Sutro Tunnel, the route of the V & T Railroad, the Comstock water system, and the log flumes.

55

hot fluids (450-575 °F) rose upward through the faulted andesite and granodiorite and crystallized as metallic gold and sulfides of silver (argentite), zinc (sphalerite), lead (galena), copper (chalcopyrite), and iron (pyrite), along with abundant quartz and calcite. Ore formed during repeated movements on the faults.

The Comstock, Silver City, and Occidental faults are the major structures that predate or are synchronous with this mineralization. Veins that formed along these faults persist from the present surface to more than 3,300 feet deep. Shafts were dug 3,200 feet deep to recover the ore, making some of the Comstock mines the deepest in the world at that time.

HISTORY OF THE COMSTOCK LODE

The story of the Comstock Lode began in 1849 south of Virginia City near the town of Dayton, an immigrant stop then known as Spafford Hall's Station. Passing immigrants began to pan the streams nearby in what came to be called Gold Canyon (this route will pass Gold Canyon in a few miles). From 1852 to 1855, perhaps 100 prospectors washed the gravel of Gold Canyon pocketing about $5.00 a day—but the bonanza lay farther up the hill toward Mount Davidson.

Early in 1859, gold was discovered by two independent parties at both ends of the Comstock fault (about a mile apart). In January 1859, James Finney (familiarly known as "Old Virginny"), Jack Yount, Alec Henderson, and John Bishop were the first to stake claims on the south end of the fault at Gold Hill. Patrick McLaughlin and Peter O'Riley, who had been panning up Sixmile Canyon, started a small placer operation on June 8, 1859 on the north end of the fault near Ophir Ravine. This was the beginning of the Ophir mine and marked the beginning of mining on the Comstock Lode. Only after a few years of work did it become apparent that these two strikes were located on the same mineralized vein.

Miners honored Old Virginny by naming the town after him. He profited less from his Comstock interests than any other locator and was killed in 1861 by being thrown from a horse. The "Comstock" name was less formally established. Henry T.P. Comstock was a Canadian fur trader and trapper who drifted into Gold Canyon in the mid-1850s taking over the Grosh brothers' papers and claims after their deaths (refer to page 69 for more on the Grosh brothers). He had the habit of staking claims on just about any unoccupied ground, and insisted that McLaughlin and O'Riley had actually made their discovery on his property. To keep the peace, they cut this local loudmouth in on their discovery and he made it his business to make sure everyone along the entire length of the new mining district knew it was "his" property too. Thus, the other miners came to call it Comstock's Lode. Although production from the Ophir mine topped $400 million, none of the original discoverers retained possession of their claims long enough to reap any appreciable monetary reward. They all died penniless.

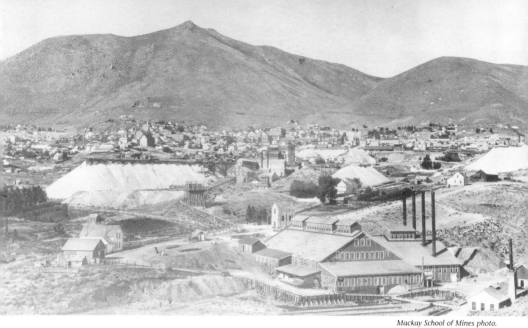

Virginia City looking west. The California pan mill is in the foreground and the 80-stamp crushing plant is beyond the pan mill. Crushed ore was flumed to the mill.

The central part of Virginia City in 1878 from the water flume, looking eastward down Sixmile Canyon. The rebuilt Catholic Church marks the southern limit of the great fire of October 26, 1875.

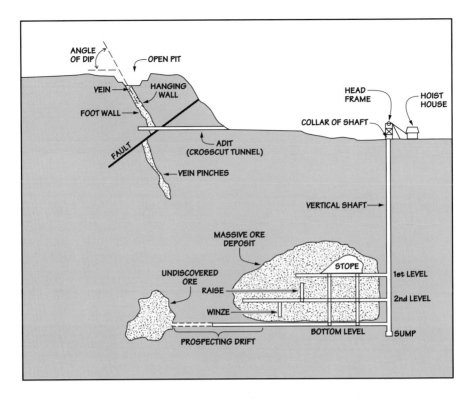

Various mining methods used on the Comstock Lode.

As the 1859 miners washed the gravel for placer gold, they were impeded by a blue clay that clogged their equipment. They continued to discard it until some was taken to an assay office in Grass Valley, California, where the results showed that the miners had been throwing away ore worth up to $3,000/ton in silver and $900/ton in gold. When this news leaked out, the "rush to Washoe" was on.

In 1871, the Crown Point Bonanza, a concentration of gold and silver found 1,000 feet below the surface, yielded $35 million, boosting that mine's stock from $2.00 to over $1,800 per share. The Big Bonanza discovered in 1873 by John Mackay and his associates on the 1,400-foot level of the Consolidated Virginia mine produced $105 million. The mining boom continued through 1878 as discoveries were made deeper along the Lode.

Production peaked in 1876, and by the 1880s all mining, except for a few high-grade pockets in the East Vein Zone, was confined to old stope fill and low-grade ore in the upper levels. By World War II production had all but ceased. A brief flurry of exploration activity began again in the mid-1960s. In 1979, Houston International Minerals Corp. began mining in the former Consolidated Imperial pit in Gold Hill, but closed the mine in 1981 after losing a battle with the local residents to enlarge their pit, which would have required relocating the Greiner's Bend section of State Route 342 at Gold Hill. The Comstock Lode continues to attract the interest of miners.

MINING CONDITIONS

Mining on the Comstock was exceedingly hazardous. The deeper mines were hot and humid; air temperatures in the workings commonly reached 100 to 125 °F and rock temperatures as high as 167 °F were recorded. Hot water was a plague of the lower depths of these mines and fog was ever present in the upper levels, where the rising hot, humid air mixed with the cold mountain air. Many men suffered pneumonia from these temperature variations. The moisture rotted the timbers and the rocks swelled and crumbled. Rockfalls and cave-ins were a constant hazard. Air circulation was very poor. Along with the stench from human and animal feces and residual vapors from blasting, the buildup of carbon dioxide within the mines from these sources caused dizziness, headaches, nausea, and weakness. More men died from poor air circulation than from any other cause in the early years of mining on the Comstock. The most serious ailment was silicosis, caused by breathing the high-silica (quartz) dust. The disease varied in severity, but often led to the fatal respiratory conditions of pneumonia and tuberculosis.

COMSTOCK ENGINEERING INNOVATIONS

The boom years of 1863 through 1880 brought about major engineering innovations to help solve some of the problems of deep underground mining. Some of these are still in use today.

Dynamite, composed of nitroglycerine mixed with stabilizing fillers such as sawdust, was invented in 1866 by Swedish chemist Alfred Nobel. By 1868, dynamite had replaced black powder as the principal blasting agent in the mines. Nobel's invention brought him fortune as well as fame. He later used part of his wealth to establish the Nobel prizes.

The Burleigh drill, which was powered by compressed air, greatly reduced the time and effort needed to drill blast holes in the rock. As a side benefit, it also helped to ventilate the mines.

Braided, flat, woven wire cable was first developed in 1863 by English immigrant Andrew S. Hallidie of San Francisco to hoist the heavy ore buckets up from the deep Sierra Nevada mine. The cable was 4 inches wide, 1/2 inch thick, and could raise up to 10 tons of weight. Hallidie later invented the endless underground cable and mechanical gripping device still used by cable cars in San Francisco.

The square-set timbering method was developed in 1860 for the Ophir Mining Company by Phillip Deidesheimer, a young immigrant engineer, especially for the type of soft, wet, crumbly rock encountered on the Comstock Lode. The clay-rich rock would expand with the addition of water, or contract and crumble when dried out, causing the rock mass to shift, breaking normal timbering and causing cave-ins. Deidesheimer's system later was adopted in mines around the world. Had he patented his invention, he would have received millions in royalties. He once told his best friend, "If all goes well and these square sets protect the lives of the miners, what more could a man ask for?" (Earl, 1986). Examples of square-set timbers are on display at the Nevada State Museum in Carson City (see page 140).

Near the end of this trip, in Washoe Valley, and on Trip C (Lake Tahoe) there will be more discussion on the effects of having to provide all the lumber for these square-sets and to fuel the boilers for the huge Cornish pumps.

Cornish pumps, used in the deep tin mines of Cornwall, were developed to their maximum here on the Comstock, but they still could barely keep up with the amount of water issuing from the depths of the mines. The pumps consisted of a series of huge hydraulic pistons, placed at vertical intervals of about 250 feet, which lifted the water from station to station into large temporary storage tanks set in chambers adjacent to the shaft. The water was

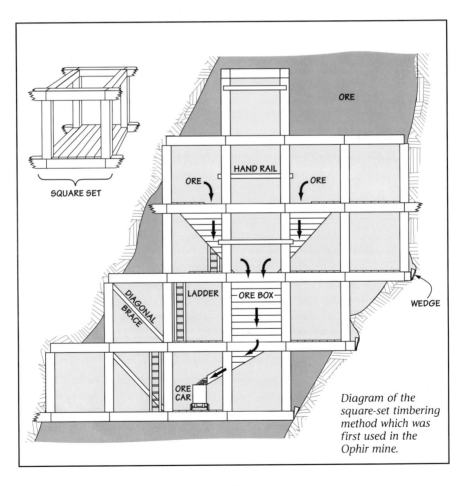

Diagram of the square-set timbering method which was first used in the Ophir mine.

Cornish pump installed in the Union Shaft in 1878. The flywheel weighed 110 tons.

forced by a piston pump plunger from the lowest station, to the next higher station, and so forth, until it reached the surface.

THE SUTRO TUNNEL

Around 1863, Adolph Sutro, another German engineer, conceived the idea of digging a tunnel into the Flowery Range to drain the Comstock mines at the 1,650-foot level. The mines would benefit by being ventilated and drained of the constant flow of hot water. Sutro hoped to profit by charging the mines to truck ore out of their lower levels through his tunnel, and perhaps strike a rich vein himself in the process. Initially, support was strong from the mine owners, the banks, the Nevada legislature (which in 1865 gave Sutro an exclusive franchise to the tunnel for 50 years), and the U.S. Congress (which passed the Sutro Tunnel Act in 1866); however, it weakened just 2 years later when the bankers (led by William Sharon, head of the Bank of California in Virginia City) and mine owners decided Virginia City would lose its inflow of cash to the mills and related businesses which would be built at the entrance to Sutro's Tunnel just east of Dayton near the Carson River.

In 1869, however, the miners rallied behind Sutro after a bad underground fire in the Yellow Jacket mine killed many men. Money to build the tunnel was secured from a London bank, other European sources, and the miners' union. Work finally began on the tunnel in October 1869.

The tunnel reached the Savage Shaft in July 1878, almost 9 years after ground-breaking, but by then the Comstock mines had progressed as much as 1,500 feet below the level which the tunnel was to drain, and the

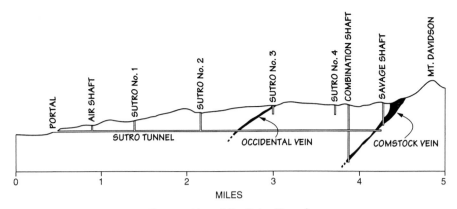

Cross section of the Sutro Tunnel.

bonanza days were over. Had the tunnel been completed in the early 1870s, it would have saved the mining companies millions of dollars in pumping costs alone.

The Sutro Tunnel runs in a straight line from the eastern front of the Flowery Range (located 1 mile north of U.S. 50 and 2.25 miles northeast of Dayton) to a drift on the Savage Shaft, a distance of 20,498 feet (almost 4 miles). It was 8 to 9 feet wide and 7 feet high. In all, the tunnel cost $6.5 million, including interest, to complete. It was never paid back in royalties after completion of the tunnel. Sutro quietly sold his stock in the tunnel shortly after it was finished, netting less than $1 million. He invested this money in San Francisco real estate and became a multimillionaire. He became active in politics and served as the mayor of San Francisco from 1895 to 1897. His health began to fail during his term as mayor, and he died in 1898.

The Comstock water supply, another fascinating chapter of engineering genius during this period, will be addressed later at mile 3.7 on page 84 where the trip route crosses over the inverted siphon at the watermaster's house at Lakeview Summit.

In 1876, Virginia City's best year, the population peaked at 25,000 permanent residents, and the mines produced over $36 million. Another 9,000 to 10,000 people resided in neighboring Gold Hill. Virginia City had over 100 saloons, six churches, four banks, Piper's Opera House, and the V & T Railroad with as many as 50 trains passing through town in a single day. A great fire destroyed almost three-quarters of the city in 1875, and although rebuilding began immediately, the rich ore discoveries were diminishing fast. By 1890 only 6,000 residents remained and by 1923 the population had dwindled to 1,500.

The impact the Comstock Lode had on Nevada is summed up by Glass and Glass (1975): "Discovery and subsequent development of the Comstock Lode constituted the most important event in Nevada's early history. Nevada became world famous, established itself as a state of the Union, helped to finance the Civil War, contributed to the building of the West, and gave wealth, poverty, fame or notoriety to hundreds of people during the boom years." For a wealth of published information on the Comstock Lode, see the publications by E. Lord, G.H. Smith, J.D. Galloway, and H.A. Shamberger listed in the Bibliography near the end of this book.

0.0 **Proceed about 1 mile south to the junction of C Street and State Route 341 and pull off to the right, opposite the Fourth Ward School. Reset odometer to 0.0.**

On the right is the Loring pit, named for W. J. Loring, mine manager. It was mined by the Arizona Comstock Mining Company during the 1930s for low-grade silver ore valued at $2 to $3 per ton. About 460,000 tons of ore were extracted yielding $1,437,000. In 1981, the Chollar raise was opened in the bottom of the pit by the United Mining Company as a ventilation and escape shaft for its New Savage mine (the portal of the mine is located to the east below F Street). Underground mining at the New Savage began in 1979. Production began in April 1983, and ended in April 1985 due to declining gold prices.

Continue straight ahead (south) on State Route 342 to Gold Hill and Silver City. This area between Virginia City and Gold Hill is called "The Divide."

Aerial view of Greiner's Bend looking northwest. The Houston International Minerals (formerly Consolidated Imperial) pit is on the left.

0.1 Gold Hill, and Ophir (Jumbo) Grade Historical Marker on the right (just before the maintenance station). The earliest miners on the Comstock had to break the ore into small pieces and haul it in boxes or sacks by mule over the Sierra Nevada to the nearest market, San Francisco. The Ophir Grade was built in 1860 by the Ophir Mining Company to haul ore westward down to Washoe Lake for milling at the Ophir mill (see photo on page 94). Lumber was transported from the sawmills in Washoe City back up the grade to the Comstock mines. When the V & T Railroad was built in 1871, Virginia City was linked to the mills on the Carson River and the road was no longer needed. A brief mining boom in the Jumbo district, over the hill to the west, opened the grade again in the early 20th century.

The road descends steeply into the head of Gold Canyon, which stretches about 6 miles southeastward to Dayton and the Carson River, via Greiner's Bend. Greiner's Bend was named for John and William Greiner whose home on this bend became a showplace because of its beautiful front yard.

0.5 The huge pit on the right was last mined by Houston International Minerals. This is the former site of "Gold Hill," the original discovery site of gold in quartz on the south end of the Comstock Lode by James Finney and his associates in 1859. Later it was opened up as the Consolidated Imperial pit. Houston renewed mining here in 1979, processing thousands of tons of low-grade ore at its cyanide plant at American Flat. The mine was closed in 1981 after Houston lost its proposal with the townsfolk to relocate the highway so that the pit could be enlarged.

0.7 The red building to the right is the Gold Hill Depot for the V & T Railroad. A passenger steam train, using historic V & T rolling stock and engine runs a route from Virginia City to Gold Hill, the only part

V & T steam train on the track between Virginia City and Gold Hill. V & T rolling stock follows the historic V & T route today.

Larry Garside photo.

64

Upper Gold Hill in 1875, looking toward the Divide. The Yellow Jacket hoisting works are at the lower right.

of the former route that has track. Just beyond the depot is the Yellow Jacket inclined shaft and headframe and Crown Point Ravine. The V & T crossed the ravine on an impressive 85-foot-high and 500-foot-long trestle (see photo on page 83). The former route of the railroad hugs the base of the mountain to the west (right) for the next several miles and will be out of sight most of the time.

Fort Homestead stood on the hill to the left and is marked today by a flagpole. The site was leased from the Homestead Mining Company—thus, the name. Established in the summer of 1864 to relieve overcrowding of volunteer troops at Fort Churchill, the fort was actually "more of a patriotic rallying point than a true military compound, although it did boast at least one cannon" (McDonald, 1982). Nothing remains of the compound, which was abandoned in the early 1870s.

0.8 Entering the town of Gold Hill, which once had a population of 9,000 residents. The former California Bank building is on the right, along with Nevada's oldest building, the famous Gold Hill Hotel built in 1859. Stop and browse through the bookstore, visit the old bar and Great Room, stay the night in the refurbished rooms, or have a delicious meal in the elegant dining room.

*Gold Hill Hotel in 1965. Originally built in 1859 and called
Vesey's Gold Hill Bar and Hotel.*

Just beyond the hotel, also on the right, are the gray buildings of
the Crown Point mill, which represent a brief period (1933 to 1942) of
mining and milling revitalization on the Comstock. Built in 1935, the
mill processed ore from the nearby Yellow Jacket and Crown Point
claims and, later, from the Con Imperial pit, by using gravity in the
process—the ore dropped from one stage to the next in an ever more
refined state. The efficiency of this mill operation was very high, aver-
aging a 90 percent recovery rate for both gold and silver. The mill ran
until 1943. In the first three years of production, 115,000 tons of ore
were milled to recover $708,000.

1.5 On the left is the metal headframe of the New York mine built in
1913, and beyond it is the wooden headframe of the Keystone Shaft
which is representative of the mining equipment dotting the landscape in the late 19th century. Both were used to transport men
and equipment into the depths of the mines, and to raise ore to the
surface.

The Silver City fault is on the right side of the road here. Dirt roads
in the hills above to the right lead past some of the most famous mines
of the Comstock: Baltimore, Knickerbocker, Overman, Caledonia, and
Keystone. Most of these were in production as late as 1942.

1.9 Hartford Hill is on the right and is composed of ash-flow tuff about 21 million years old. Just ahead, at the base of the hill is the Lucerne Cut, a mineralized zone on the Silver City fault, exposing basaltic andesite.

This was the site of open-pit gold mining operations in the 1880s, 1900-1909, 1940s, 1950s, and early 1990s. From the 1920s to the 1950s, 200,000 tons of ore yielded $1,200,000. Between 1989 and 1990, the Oliver Hills Mining Company removed 120,000 tons of ore containing 0.038 to 0.048 ounces of gold per ton. This recent work exposed older underground tunnels now visible as round openings on the back wall. Note the remains (half-way up the hill) of the Hartford Hill Mining Company cyanide mill which operated from 1935 to 1940.

2.8 Entering Lyon County and passing through Devil's Gate composed of andesite. Mesozoic metavolcanic rocks are exposed in the lower part of the roadcuts on the right.

Devil's Gate was the site of a toll station on the Virginia City-Dayton Toll Road in the 1860s. The present route closely follows the original toll road. Before construction of the V & T Railroad in 1870, this road carried the slow, heavy traffic of animal teams pulling wagonloads of ore (at $5.50 per ton) from the Comstock mines down to the Carson River mills for processing. The teams returned to the Comstock with loads of timber (at $15 per cord) from the Lake Tahoe

The New York mine in 1995.

67

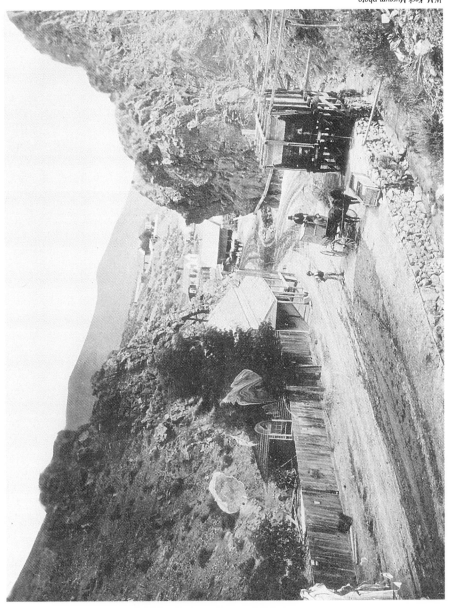

Devil's Gate looking south in the 1800s.

W.M. Keck Museum photo.

basin to be used for fuel and square-sets in the mines. Every other kind of food, merchandise, and machinery needed in the boomtowns was also transported up this road. The toll road cost $2,000 to $3,000 per mile to build. The teamsters' haulage rates were two to three times higher than those later charged by the railroad.

A small community grew up around the toll station in late 1859. Extra teams were corralled here, and the area was a reputed hangout for bandits. Andrew Marsh wrote the following description of Devil's Gate in the early 1860s: "It was dark before we reached this point, and the scene impressed me as strangely weird and almost diabolical. All around us was heard the clatter and thunder of quartz mills, from each gleamed the furnace fires like the eyes of demons..."

2.9 Entering Silver City. This is the third largest community on the Comstock and Silver City faults, and was settled before Virginia City. Most of the gold and silver produced here came from within 300 feet of the surface on the Silver City fault, although some of the mines explored to depths of over 800 feet. Most of the ore-producing veins on the fault varied from less than 1 foot to 3 or 4 feet wide. In some places the ore reached 40 feet in width. The veins were generally lens-shaped and pinched out laterally and at depth.

3.1 Grosh Brothers' monument is on the right. Hosea Grosh and his brother Ethan Allen began placer mining in Gold Canyon in 1852. They were intelligent and systematic miners and might have been the first to discover the Comstock, but they both died in 1857 (Hosea of blood poisoning from a self-inflicted pick wound in his foot, and Ethan Allan in a Sierran winter storm). They had good shows on their "monster ledge" which was the Silver City fault, but it would never produce the riches that the Comstock did. In 1865, an impressive monument was placed on Hosea's grave in the cemetery east of town by a member of Abraham Lincoln's cabinet.

3.3 American Ravine is off to the right. About a mile up the canyon is the site of the American Flat mill and American City. American City was established in 1864. Around 1921, the United Comstock Merger cyanide mill was built to process several million tons of ore from mines in Gold Hill (owned by United Comstock Mines Company) and in Virginia City (owned by the Comstock Merger Mines Company). The mines and mill operated for several years until the price of silver dropped from over a dollar to $0.28 per ounce. The first power lines over the Sierra Nevada provided electricity for this mill.

3.4 Outcrops along the road to the right are Mesozoic metavolcanic rocks.

Donovan's mill is on the left. The oldest portion of this mill, dating back to 1890, is a small-scale, 10-stamp operation. In 1900, the mill operators experimented with the cyanidation process to refine the ore. First the ore was crushed into fine particles (inside the large corrugated metal building), then a mixture of water, lime, and sodium cyanide was added to it. The separation process was continued outside in the large 100-ton capacity redwood tanks (there were originally five tanks). As the mixture was gently stirred, the gold and silver dissolved in the cyanide solution. Inside the main building, further refinement took place, extracting the silver and gold from the cyanide solution. Remarkably, this process extracted 93 percent of the gold and silver from the rock. It was one of the longest-running cyanide mills on the Comstock, operating from 1900 to 1959.

3.5 Historical marker on the right commemorates the McCones Foundries. Ahead, on the hillside to the right is the Dayton mill (formerly the Flowery mill), which was moved here in 1932 from Sixmile Canyon by the Dayton Consolidated Mines Company. The mill processed ore from the company's many claims on the Comstock, using the cyanide process and additional flotation cells. Before the mill closed in 1942, a total of 185,428 tons of ore was processed from the Dayton mine alone, with a yield of $1,791,000, mostly in gold.

This marks the south end of the productive zone of the Silver City fault.

3.6 Junction with State Route 341 on the left. State Route 342 ends here. Continue straight ahead on State Route 341. Gold Canyon bends to the southeast here. About 1.5 miles downstream are the original Dayton placer gold workings.

The hills to the right are composed mainly of ash-flow tuff. The many prospect holes dotting the hills reflect the search for a southern extension of the Comstock Lode.

Ahead and to the left are the Pine Nut Mountains. In the distance at 1:00 is the high Carson Range forming the eastern boundary of the Lake Tahoe basin and the Sierra Nevada.

6.1 The Pony Express Trail between Dayton and Carson City crossed the road here. The rest of its route followed the California Emigrant Trail (now U.S. 50) along the Carson River.

The dominant vegetation in this area is sagebrush and desert needlegrass. Below a dense clay subsoil a silica-cemented lime layer restricts water and root penetration, thus limiting vegetation growth.

6.5 Junction with U.S. 50. Turn left for an optional trip to Dayton and the Sutro Tunnel

or

Turn right to Carson City and reset odometer to 0.0 just as you turn onto U.S. 50. Turn to page 74 to continue the log to Carson City.

Donovan's mill in Silver City.

The Dayton mill in Silver City.

Placer mining in Gold Canyon below Silver City at the Briggs millsite (1874).

OPTIONAL TRIP TO DAYTON AND
THE SUTRO TUNNEL:

Turn left and travel east on U.S. 50. In about 1 mile, mounds of dredge tailings from placer operations in Gold Canyon are visible about 1/2 mile away on the left. This is the general location of the first gold discovery in 1848. Ten more years of panning up Gold Canyon led to the discovery of the Comstock Lode.

A long line of dumps at the base of the Flowery Range east of Dayton mark the Sutro townsite.

Continue another 2 miles to Dayton, formerly called Spafford Hall's Station, located on the Carson River route of the Overland California emigrant trail in the late 1840s. A large community of Chinese settled here in the 1850s after being brought out to dig the Dayton Ditch, and the settlement became known as "Chinatown." The site was almost deserted before the discovery of the Comstock Lode. The town was named "Dayton" in 1861 in honor of John Day, county surveyor, and was an important mill center for Comstock ores for several decades. It was the Lyon County seat from 1861 to 1911. Most of the historic buildings date from 1870, the year of the second great fire.

Note the historical marker (on the right) at the junction of U.S. 50 and Dayton Valley Road.

Entrance to the Sutro Tunnel at the base of the Flowery Range.

Nevada Historical Society photo.

Turn right on Dayton Valley Road and travel one block to the Carson River bridge. Emigrant wagons were parked under the cottonwoods for miles along the Carson River in the mid-19th century.

Return to downtown Dayton. Points of interest include the Dayton Historical Society Museum, Dayton Museum, Dayton Public School, Odeon

Hall, Union Hotel, Bluestone Building, Dayton City Park, and the Dayton cemetery. The ruins of the Rock Point mill (built in 1861) are on the left as you proceed east out of Dayton.

To reach the entrance of the Sutro Tunnel, travel 2.2 miles east of the Rock Point mill (on the east side of Dayton) on U.S. 50. Turn left (north) on the unpaved road just before the Sutro Historical Marker. Travel about a mile to the tunnel entrance at the base of the Flowery Range. **This is private property. Tours may be arranged by calling a phone number posted near the entrance to the house.**

End of optional trip to Dayton. Retrace route back to the junction of U.S. 50 and State Route 341 (to Virginia City).

Reset odometer to 0.0. at the junction of U.S. 50 and State Route 341.

0.0 **Continue west on U.S. 50 toward Carson City.**

The route crosses an old valley that was the major drainageway for this area before the Carson River cut its present canyon through the north end of the Pine Nut Mountains to the left (south).

0.2 Entering Mound House (elev. 4,913 feet).

0.5 The route passes through Tertiary mudflow breccias.

0.6 Note the mining operation at 2:00. Light-colored deposits of gypsum occur in Jurassic(?) metamorphosed igneous rocks. The gypsum was milled for plaster at a nearby plant along the V & T Railroad from 1913 to 1920, with a total production of about $452,000. Local well water contains high concentrations of calcium, magnesium, and sulfate related to the gypsum deposits.

1.3 Mound House Historical Marker on the right. Mound House was settled in the late 1860s around Mound Station, a toll stop on the Carson-Comstock stage road. The V & T Railroad arrived here in 1869, and in 1871 Mound House was established as a transfer point for people and freight traveling by coach or wagon to Dayton, Pine Grove, or Sutro. For the first few years it was no more than a wood and water stop, and began to decline when the Comstock mines ran out of ore. In 1881, the V & T finished a narrow gauge line, the Carson and Colorado, to the mining camps of southwestern Nevada and southeastern California. Business boomed for about three years, but when the Tonopah and Goldfield silver and gold strikes occurred just after 1900, Mound House became an intolerable bottleneck in the busy railway system. In 1905, Southern Pacific, which had acquired the Carson and Colorado, built a standard gauge track (the Hazen cutoff). This ended the interchange here. The V & T ended all operations in this area in 1939.

1.7 Here at Highlands Drive, the V & T Railroad crossed the highway and followed the Carson River to the mills.

2.1 Leaving Lyon County and entering Carson City.

3.0 The road passes through a thin flow of Pleistocene (1.4 million years old) basalt which issued from McClelland Peak, a now partially dissected volcanic vent about 3 miles to the north.

4.1 The historical marker commemorating the Carson River mills is on the left side of the highway.

MILLING THE COMSTOCK ORES

By the end of 1861, more than 76 mills with a total of 1,153 stamps had been built for crushing and separating Comstock ore. These mills were located first in Virginia City, Sixmile Canyon, Gold Canyon, and Washoe Valley, and later along the Carson River from Dayton to Empire. They had a combined capacity for crushing 1,200 tons of ore daily, but there was ore for only about half of them. Many had been built entirely on speculation. After 1878, the mills began closing down as the Comstock mines failed.

Recovery of gold and silver from the Comstock ores presented a formidable challenge to the miners of the 1860s. More complex than the easily milled ores of California, Comstock silver ores required treatment by methods reminiscent of those of medieval alchemy. Experimenting to devise a process that would efficiently release the gold and silver from the enclosing rock extended over several years and culminated in the development of the "Washoe Process" in 1860 (developed chiefly by millman A.B. Paul) and the "Washoe Pan Mill" (invented by a few ingenious California mill builders). The Washoe Process was a mechanical combination of two other centuries-old processes (of crushing the ore, and chemically recovering the precious metals) that early Comstock miners had been using. The new Washoe Process accomplished in 6 hours what had formerly taken 4 to 6 weeks, and recovered a significantly greater percentage of the precious metals.

Previous to the Washoe Process, the early miners crushed the ore in arrastras, or crude drag-stone mills. The pulverized ore was mixed with water, mercury, salt, and copper sulfate. This mixture was spread on an open floor exposed to the sun's heat, and was turned with shovels or trampled with stock animals. Eventually, the metal sulfides in the ore were converted to chlorides, liberating the precious metals. Under the proper conditions, the gold and silver in the ore readily united with the mercury

The Brunswick mill on the Carson River.

W.M. Keck Museum photos.

to form amalgam, an alloy of mercury and the precious metals. This was the simplest, cheapest, and most efficient process known to the small mine operator.

At a typical 1870s Carson River (Washoe Pan) mill, the ore was delivered by the V & T Railroad and dumped into huge hoppers. The Carson River provided the steady force needed to turn the huge water wheels that powered the mechanized stamps (huge pestles raised by water or steam power). The stamps crushed the ore into sand-sized particles. This material was mixed with salt, mercury, and water in huge, steam-heated pans. Large internal blades stirred the mixture for 6 to 12 hours until the precious metals became trapped in the mercury. The mercury-gold-silver amalgam settled to the bottom and was collected. Finally, the mercury was boiled off in retorts, leaving only the doré (nearly pure gold and silver), and the mercury vapor was condensed and reused.

During the stamping stage, much of the ore escaped being crushed into the optimum sand-sized particles. These grains passed through the mills and were discharged into the Carson River and surrounding canyons as waste. It is estimated that 3 million ounces of gold and 64 million ounces of silver were lost. Attempts have been made to obtain permits to dredge the river for its high gold and silver content.

It is estimated that about 15 million pounds of mercury was also released into the environment largely between 1860 and 1895. The persistence of mercury in the environment has made the impact of the amalgam milling operations in this region enormous. Mercury-contaminated tailings (waste sediments produced from a mill), soil, sediment, air, and water can be found in Virginia City, Silver City, Gold Canyon, Sixmile and Sevenmile Canyons, Sixmile alluvial fan, Dayton, Fallon, Washoe Valley, Pleasant Valley, the Carson River and its floodplains, and Lahontan Reservoir.

Mercury concentrations as high as 4,600 ppm have been measured in Sixmile Canyon tailings, 887 ppm in Carson River bank sediments, 45 ppm in Washoe Valley, 99 ppm in Lahontan Reservoir, and 350 ppm in Carson River bank sediments northeast of Fallon. Geochemical studies show that 90 percent or more of the mercury in tailings is still present in elemental form, and that mercury and silver are slowly dissolving out of upstream amalgam particles and are becoming sorbed to fine-grained sediments being transported downstream and increasing the concentrations of mercury in the water (after Miller and others, 1993).

Portions of this area have been declared a superfund site by the U.S. Environmental Protection Agency—the first in Nevada—and must be cleaned up or stabilized as much as possible. Needless to say, the mercury is going to be around for a very long time. To significantly disturb the river may be disastrous to the environment downstream. In areas above the water table, mercury-laden soil can be dug up and removed, and replaced with new topsoil.

5.0 The Nevada State Maximum Security Prison is located at the base of Prison Hill at 9:00. In the early 1860s, Abraham Curry operated a hotel and swimming pools at the warm springs located along the fault on the northwest side of the Hill. Curry's Warm Springs Hotel was leased in 1862 to serve as the Territorial Prison with Curry as its warden. The state later purchased the property.

Well-cemented late Pliocene or Pleistocene sandstone was quarried and faced at the north end of the hill by the inmates for use in constructing buildings in Carson City (including the Capitol, the U.S. Mint, and the prison), Reno (including the main gate to the University described on page 19) and Virginia City, and the Brunswick mill (Carson River).

Fossilized footprints and skeletal remains of many species of birds and mammals, including the ground sloth, mammoth, horse, bison, deer, peccary, wolf, and possibly sabre-tooth tiger are preserved in the sandstone which formed in a lake that occupied this valley.

6.7 Just beyond the Saliman Road intersection at 2:00, note the Holocene fault scarp in basin fill across the vacant lot. The scarp is 30 to 35 feet high and houses are built on the upthrown block. This fault scarp is located on the southern edge of the Carson lineament, one of several northeast-trending structural zones recognized in the western Basin and Range province.

Faults along this zone may have over 300 feet of vertical displacement along with lateral displacement, making them oblique-slip faults (diagrams of types of faults are on page 10). This lineament has been interpreted as a left-lateral compliment to the Walker Lane, a major northwest-trending right-lateral fault zone. These near-surface faults may reflect movement on deeper strike-slip faults controlling Cenozoic north-trending horst and graben development.

Nevada Historical Society photo.

CARSON CITY

Carson City is the state capital and is situated in Eagle Valley, a structural depression bounded by the Pine Nut Mountains on the east (left), the Virginia Range on the north (right), and the Carson Range on the west.

Settlement began in the valley around 1851 when W.L. "Frank" Hall and several business associates established a trading post on the California Emigrant Trail. Ranch houses, a hotel, stores, saloons, and livery stables were built. A few years later, Hall's property was bought out by Abe Curry and his partners for $500 in gold plus some

Prehistoric footprints at the Nevada State Prison unearthed in 1908.

Holocene fault (light-colored by dry cheatgrass) just northwest of the intersection of U.S. 50 and Saliman Road. The house is on the upthrown fault block.

horses. Curry's townsite was platted in 1858 and included a "capitol square." The village was named in honor of John Frémont's famous scout, Christopher "Kit" Carson. The Comstock Lode was discovered a few months later, and Carson City soon replaced Genoa as the transportation and freight center for this region.

In 1861, the first Territorial Legislature met in Curry's Warm Springs Hotel and created Ormsby County, with Carson City as its seat. Major William M. Ormsby, killed in the 1860 Pyramid Lake Indian War (refer to page 168), had been one of Carson City's prominent citizens. In 1864, Nevada became the 36th state to enter the Union, with Carson City as its capital. James W. Nye, a politician from New York, was appointed by President Abraham Lincoln as the first Territorial Governor of Nevada. He later became one of Nevada's first U.S. Senators.

Agriculture was very important in this area in the 1850s; beginning in the 1860s, however, the Comstock mines (followed by the Tonopah and Goldfield booms in the early 20th century) were the most important element of Carson City's economy. Along with being a freight, railroad, and stageline center, Carson City was a terminus of the flumes bringing timber to the Comstock from Lake Tahoe.

The decline of the Comstock mines in the 1880s greatly affected Carson City's economy, but the ongoing business of government was a steadying factor as trade and traffic declined.

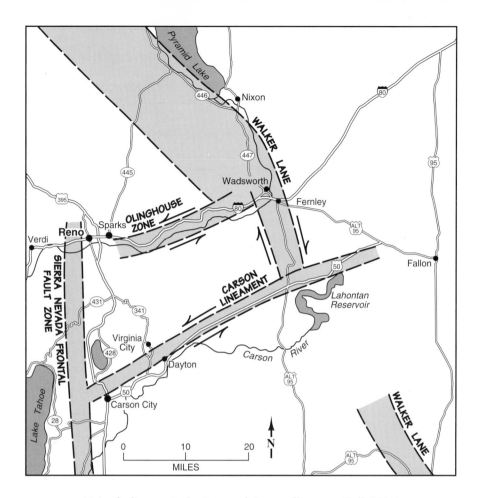

Major fault zones in the Reno and Carson City areas (Bell, 1984).

7.4 Stewart Street intersection. To the left is the site of the V & T round-house built in 1872. Ten tracks converged on a turntable here. The machine shop, foundry, and repair shops extended for a block and a half, and were surrounded by many smaller railroad maintenance shops. Carson City was the main headquarters for the V & T Railroad. By 1874, 36 trains a day passed through here traveling east to Mound House and Virginia City, and north to Reno. An extension was built south to Minden in Carson Valley in 1914.

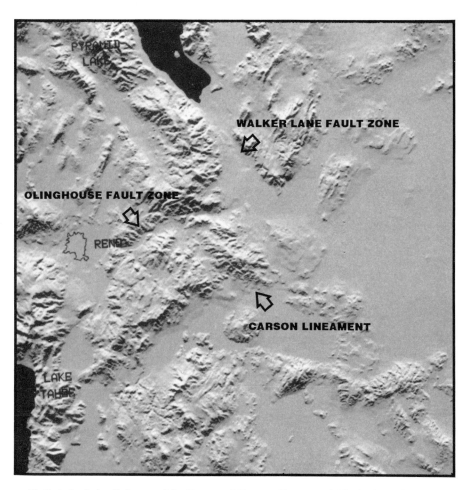

Digital shaded relief map of the Reno and Carson City areas (U.S. Geological Survey, unpublished), showing major fault zones (Bell, 1984).

THE VIRGINIA AND TRUCKEE RAILROAD

After years of discontent over stiff freight charges levied by the teamsters, a number of groups initiated proposals to construct a railroad system in this region to link the mines, cities, and logging and milling centers. The Nevada Legislature granted charters to various promoters who wanted to build the railroad, but none of them managed to begin construction before the deadline mandated in the contract.

In the spring of 1864, the Bank of California opened a branch office in Virginia City, with William Sharon as head agent. Sharon soon became the driving force behind the idea to build a railroad from the Comstock mines to the Carson River mills. As head of the bank in Virginia City, he realized that what was good for the prosperity of the mines, was even better for the prosperity of the bank; more economical ways had to be found to get the ore to the mills and supplies to the mines if mining on the Comstock was to remain profitable.

In 1865, he met in San Francisco with Darius Ogden Mills (President of the Bank of California) and William C. Ralston (cashier for the bank and a financial genius) to convince them of the need for this railroad. They agreed, and all that remained to be done was to locate the route for the railroad and apply for the charter to build it, but Sharon's plan was much broader. He meant to acquire the wealth of the Comstock for the Bank of California.

Beebe and Clegg wrote the following account in their book, *Virginia and Truckee*. Sharon undertook and accomplished "one of the shrewdest financial coups of all the buccaneering sagas of nineteenth century American finance. He set about acquiring for the bank possession of all the reducing mills in the Nevada bonanzas. Most of these were in hard straits due to the declining production of the mines, and with infinite guile, Sharon allowed their owners to overextend themselves and write overdrafts against the Bank's Virginia City branch until, turning on the mill owners with the ferocity of the grey wolf, he was able to foreclose on seven of the biggest mills on the banks of the Carson River. These were organized into the Union Mining and Milling Company, and, within two years were joined by ten lesser properties, so that by the year 1869 the Bank of California, without in any way involving itself in the speculative business of mining precious metals, a form of investment which met with the implacable disapproval of Mills, still had an absolute stranglehold on the mining industry in the Comstock. Without credit from the monopolistic bank, no mine in all the Comstock could operate, and unless its ores were reduced in the mills controlled by the bank there would, it was explained, be no credit forthcoming."

As a result of these and other actions, Sharon became a powerful and detested ruler on the Comstock for the next 10 years. He continued to deal in stock speculation, which eventually brought about his downfall.

On March 6, 1868, after a number of changes were made in the route and sufficient funds were raised to assure construction of the railroad, the Nevada Legislature reissued the railroad charter to the newly incorporated Virginia and Truckee Railroad Company, with the Bank of California as major financier and builder. Sharon, a master at fundraising, managed to raise in two months the sum of $1,200,000 in personal contributions from himself, other bank heads, the mining companies, and the county governments. This insured that the "risks of constructing the road [were] equally shared, even if its direct profits were not [to be] divided" (Lord, 1883).

Surveying of the rail route began late in 1868, and construction began in Gold Hill in February 1869. Many of the workmen were Chinese, recently released from building the Central Pacific line to the north. Thirty-eight construction camps were established along the 21 miles of road to Carson City, and by early summer 1,200 men were spiking down the rails to untreated ties on the standard gauge railroad.

The builders had to deal with the 1,575-foot drop in elevation from Virginia City to the Carson River. They managed to hold the maximum descending grade to 2.2 percent by "wrapping the railroad around the hills - with a curvature equivalent to 17 complete circles in the 13.5-mile route between the two points" (Myrick, 1962). This, the toughest portion of the entire railroad, was completed at a cost of $1,750,000, or $83,000 per mile.

The first locomotive arrived in Carson City on August 6, 1869, and track laying commenced there toward Gold Hill on September 28. Henry M. Yerington was general manager and superintendent of the railroad. On November 29 of that same year, the first train ran between Carson City and Gold Hill.

The rails were made in England and shipped around Cape Horn. The locomotives arrived overland from the Baldwin Locomotive Works in Philadelphia. Three of the five locomotives were delivered to Carson City by wagon from Reno. The other two were hauled by ox-drawn wagon up the Geiger Grade to Virginia City. The ties were cut from Sierran timber, and some of the rail cars were purchased from the Central Pacific Railroad.

By January 29, 1870, the railroad was extended from Gold Hill to Virginia City, and the Comstock was finally linked to Carson City. There were six tunnels, totaling 2,400 feet.

Nevada Historical Society photo.

A V&T wood train passes over the Crown Point Ravine in Gold Hill in 1893.

83

By August 24, 1872, the Comstock and Carson City were linked to the rest of the nation by rail. The V & T connected with the Central Pacific in Reno.

When completed, the railroad stretched a total of 52.2 miles, with 37 additional miles of spurs and siding built to various mines and mills. By 1874, as many as 50 trains traveled on the line every day. During maximum traffic, the railroad operated 24 locomotives, 10 passenger cars, 4 express cars, and 361 freight cars (including ore cars). Wood, hay, machinery, and ice were the main commodities hauled from the valleys to Virginia City. Virtually all of the outgoing freight from Virginia City was ore bound for processing in the Carson River mills.

Some of the steam locomotives, coaches, and freight cars used on the V & T have been renovated and are on display in the Nevada State Railroad Museum at 2180 South Carson Street (at the southwest corner of U.S. 395 and Fairview Drive) in Carson City. The museum offers changing exhibits, train and hand-car rides, lectures, and a variety of special events.

7.6 Junction of U.S. 50 with U.S. 395.

0.0 **Reset odometer to 0.0. Turn right** and proceed north on U.S. 395 to Reno.

(*Note*: The south half of Carson City is covered in Trip C, beginning on page 139.)

0.1 The small rise in the road marks a fault scarp.

1.5 Begin climb to Lakeview Summit which separates Eagle Valley and Carson City on the south from Washoe Valley to the north. Note the old V & T railroad bed midway up the hillside to the left.

The burned area on the left was due to fire ignited by lightning strikes on June 26, 1987. Partially decomposed Cretaceous granite forms the hills in this area and can be observed in the roadcuts. **Get in the right lane.**

3.7 Lakeview Summit (elev. 5,160 feet). **Carefully turn off at the historical marker on the right.** Lakeview was established in 1872 by the Virginia and Gold Hill Water Company. It also operated as a flag station for the V & T Railroad, and was a post office from 1881 to 1883 and from 1890 to 1894. The Victorian house on the left (in the trees across the freeway) was that of the watermaster for the water company. The inverted siphon/pressure pipeline for the Comstock water supply passes under the freeway at this point.

84

Faulted and jointed Cretaceous granite at Lakeview Summit.

COMSTOCK WATER SUPPLY

As mining developed on the Comstock, water became as valuable as the ore being sought. Mountain springs, snowmelt, and tunnels dug into the mountains just couldn't meet the needs of the growing population.

In May 1862, two companies that had been collecting and distributing water to the local area were consolidated into the Virginia and Gold Hill Water Company. By the end of 1863, however, only 900,000 gallons per day could be supplied to Virginia City. Each succeeding year, as the city grew, the fear of drought increased.

Engineers had considered pumping water up from the Carson River, but found that such an undertaking was uneconomical. They turned their gaze next to the deep spring snowpack of the Carson Range.

The company chiefs retained J. B. Overton as supervisor and put him in charge of surveying, constructing, and maintaining an integrated system of dams, reservoirs, flumes, tunnels, and pipelines to carry water from the Carson Range to Virginia City.

One of the most difficult surveying problems to be solved was establishing the elevations and routes of all the water sources and conveyance structures so that the water would arrive in Gold Hill and Virginia City at the speed and in the amount desired. During this process, an even more critical engineering problem was revealed. The hydrostatic pressure that would be created in a pipeline crossing the low spot in the proposed water system at Lakeview summit was greater than any pipe had ever been subjected to. A pipeline had to be designed that could withstand these unprecedented pressures.

Hermann Schussler, a German immigrant and chief engineer for the Spring Valley Water Works of San Francisco, was called in to design the "Washoe Pressure Pipe"—an inverted siphon. He had built other pipelines to resist extreme hydrostatic pressures by using iron plates rolled to a cylindrical shape and riveted at the seams.

After the surveys and calculations were completed, it was concluded that in addition to the dams, reservoirs, and flumes, a pressure pipeline 7 miles long and 11.5 inches in diameter would be required.

Construction began in 1872. The plates used to construct the pipeline were made of English wrought iron at the Risdon Iron Works in San Francisco. They varied in thickness from 0.065 to 0.34 inches, depending on the pressures they would be subjected to. Enough overlap was left for double-riveting of the joints. This riveting was done on site during construction of the pipeline. Lead caulk was used to seal the joints, and the entire pipeline was coated inside and out with asphalt and coal tar to protect against rust.

Early in August 1873, water entered the system from Hobart Creek Reservoir (elev. 7,542 feet) 3 miles west of Lakeview Summit and flowed north down Franktown Creek for a short distance before being diverted into

A section of the first pipeline laid in 1873 to supply water to Virginia City (photo taken in 1969).

Hugh Shamberger photo.

86

the aqueduct (built at a constant elevation of 7,160 feet) which curved back to the south toward the head of the pipeline, located 1.5 miles above Lakeview. The water entered the pipeline and flowed eastward, passing through the lowest point in the system at Lakeview Summit. The water discharged from the pipeline at an elevation of 6,680 feet near the southwest end of the Virginia Range about 1 mile southwest of McClelland Peak. It flowed northeastward by flume and aqueduct around the west side of the range to the range crest (about 1 mile northeast of McClelland Peak) where it met and paralleled the Ophir Grade most of the way to water storage tanks (at an elevation of 6,480

Flumes from Hobart Creek in the Sierra Nevada and in the Virginia Range circa 1877.

feet) near Bullion Ravine above Gold Hill and near Spanish Ravine in Virginia City. The entire water system is 21 miles long and has a capacity of 2,000,000 gallons of water a day.

After the Big Bonanza was discovered in Virginia City in 1873, more aqueducts and a second pipeline were planned. These were completed late in 1875, the same year that the Great Fire leveled most of Virginia City. Later, Marlette Reservoir, located a mile west of Hobart Creek Reservoir, was deepened (by raising the dam) and connected by flumes to the existing system to provide additional water. In 1887, a third pressure pipe was laid across Lakeview next to the other two.

When completed, the water supply system included three reservoirs, over 21 miles of pressure pipes across Lakeview Summit, about 46 miles of covered box flumes, and a 3,994-foot tunnel built at elevations of between 7,000 and 8,000 feet. See map on pages 54 and 55. Additional water was obtained from flume systems originally built by lumber companies to transport timber to Carson City and Washoe Valley for milling.

Five Mile Reservoir and Ice House near Gold Hill in the Virginia Range.

Nevada Historical Society photo.

The system was improved in 1963 and serves as Virginia City's water supply system today.

3.8 **Turn right onto Eastlake Blvd. exit. At the stop sign, turn left onto Eastlake Blvd. and pass under the freeway. Turn right onto State Route 429 and proceed north.**

The route has descended into Washoe Valley, another north-trending structural depression along the east side of the Carson Range. Faults bounding the western margin of the valley at the base of the Carson Range have been active in recent times and have displaced the Pleistocene landslide deposits at the base of Slide Mountain. Washoe Lake is on the right. This shallow natural lake is a result of the saturated condition of the basin fill. It dried completely during an extreme period of drought in the 1930s, and almost completely in 1977 and the early 1990s. A state park on the east side of the lake is a popular base for wind-surfing activities, camping, and summer campfire programs.

Ore from the Comstock was transported down the Ophir (Jumbo) grade—still visible in the foothills to the right—and across a causeway built at the north end of the lake to the Ophir Mill (ahead) prior to the completion of the V & T Railroad to the mills along the Carson River.

The name "Washoe" has been given to many geographic features and places in western Nevada. The "Eastern Slope" of the Sierra Nevada had become known as Washoe and in the early 1860s there was a strong movement to call this new state Washoe, rather than Nevada. The original spelling was probably "Wassau" (other spellings include Washo, Washoo, Washiu, and Wassou), which was later Anglicized to Washoe. The name is attributed to an Indian tribe that inhabited the area. Various meanings of the name include "person," "ryegrass," or "tall bunch grass."

5.8 Turn left onto Franktown Road.

Note the great view of the landslide scar on Slide Mountain at 2:00.

The route follows the base of the Carson Range through Jeffrey pines and meadows. The burned area in the hills to the left was caused by a lightning-strike fire in 1980.

10.2 Junction with old U.S. 395. **Turn left.**

10.3 Crossing Franktown Creek and the site of Franktown.

On the left, just after crossing Franktown Creek, the abrupt break in slope is a fault scarp. The corral fence marks the boundary between the upthrown and downthrown sides of the normal fault. This is part

Washoe Lake and Slide Mountain looking northwest from Lakeview Summit.

of the Sierra Nevada frontal fault zone which marks the eastern boundary of the Sierra Nevada province. (Faults in this zone will be discussed ahead at Steamboat Hot Springs.)

FRANKTOWN

Franktown was founded by Mormons in 1852, a year after Nevada's first settlement at Genoa. In 1857, Brigham Young directed his followers to return to Salt Lake City. About 350 families sold their property, but were poorly compensated, which prompted the town's ex-leader, Orson Hyde, to later place a curse on the people of Washoe and Carson Valleys. In 1862, he read a rambling letter containing the curse to the Utah legislature of which he was then a member. In part, it stated that if the new Franktown residents wouldn't consider paying a fair price for the land they had received, he wouldn't address it again, but warned that ..."You shall be visited of the Lord of Hosts with thunder and with earthquake and with floods...until your names are known amongst men..."

Franktown prospered with a large stamp mill to process Comstock ore, sawmills to process the lumber from the Lake Tahoe basin, the V & T Railroad, and farming until the ore ran out on the Comstock. By 1880, only five businesses were still operating here.

But disaster struck on February 2, 1881, which made folks wonder if Orson Hyde's curse had finally descended on Franktown. Heavy rain falling in the mountains caused a manmade dam about 2 miles upstream on Franktown Creek to give way. The resulting torrent destroyed most of the settlement and killed a few residents. Granodiorite boulders, gravel, and sand deposits dumped by the floodwaters are still visible along the road on the right.

10.9 Bowers Mansion State Park is on the left. The mansion is open for tours. The pool, play areas, covered picnic and barbecue areas, and the large expanse of lawns and trees make this a particularly refreshing place to visit. Geothermal water from a shallow well is used in the pools.

Note the cliff formed as part of the Sierra Nevada frontal fault zone. Hot water issues from springs in the faulted rock behind the mansion.

Bowers Mansion was built from 1861 through 1864 by Sandy and Ellen ("Eilley") Bowers, both poor workers on the Comstock who suddenly became millionaires upon the sale of their valuable mining claims. Wanting so much to be a part of the "upper class" of society, they held many parties at their mansion and were preyed upon by schemers and flatterers. Sandy died in 1868. The money dwindled quickly. The mansion was finally sold to pay off debts. Eilley lived out

Bowers Mansion in 1874.

her days telling fortunes in Virginia City. She died in 1903. The mansion was renovated into a resort for the public by Reno saloonkeeper, Henry Ritter. The warm springs were turned into swimming pools. The V & T ran special trains here for picnickers and other groups. The mansion was acquired by Washoe County in 1946 for a public museum and park.

11.2 Bowers Mansion fire station on the left.

Directly ahead, the road crosses landslide debris (granodiorite boulders, sand, and gravel) that has issued from the mouth of Ophir Canyon on the left. Note the hummocky terrain of older slide debris.

SLIDE MOUNTAIN

Slide Mountain is composed mainly of granodiorite having fractures roughly paralleling the steep southeastern face of the mountain. This provides prime conditions for landslides that can be triggered by unseasonably heavy precipitation or earthquakes—the two prime ingredients for a slide on these unstable slopes are water, which acts as a lubricant, and gravity. The material has moved downslope from an elevation of 9,400 feet to 5,000 feet.

This landscape was thought to be of glacial origin until the mid-1960s. Since then, geologists studying the degree of weathering on the slide material can count at least nine times in the past 50,000 years that Slide Mountain has had rock slides.

Members of the Washoe and Paiute tribes of the area had a name for the mountain which translated as "mountain which fell in upon itself." Their verbal records of the early nineteenth century relate at least one slide that sounds like it was the result of an earthquake.

Another slide was reported by the inhabitants of the area in November or early December of 1852. Seismic records for the area show it was caused by an earthquake, but fierce storms and blizzards were also plaguing the region at the time. In 1878, the *Carson Appeal* newspaper reported another slide that occurred on April 10, 1862. A band of Mormon immigrants was said to have been camped at the foot of the mountain and subsequently buried by the slide, but this could not be substantiated.

On July 8, 1890 Price Reservoir, now called Upper Price Lake, burst its dam and sent a 30-foot wall of water down Ophir Creek, flooding William Price's house and about 200 feet of the V & T Railroad track, located where U.S. 395 now runs. Eyewitness accounts suggest that a slide from the mountain probably triggered this event.

11.7 1983 Ophir Creek debris flow.

At 11:53 a.m. on May 30, 1983, a mass of rock, soil, and vegetation suddenly slid down the steep southeast-facing slope of Slide Mountain. The area of mass movement involved 40

A.S. Van Denburgh photo.

Aerial photo taken shortly after the 1983 Ophir Creek debris flow.

School bus and house partially buried in mud from the 1983 Ophir Creek debris flow.

to 50 acres and the movement was very swift. Much of the moving mass slid into the north half of Upper Price Lake, a small lake covering 4 to 5 acres on Ophir Creek. The sudden movement of debris into the lake created a surge of water that rapidly flowed into Lower Price Lake, and the cumulative contents of both lakes, about 20 to 30 acre-feet of muddy water, rushed down the steep (roughly 25 percent gradient) canyon of Ophir Creek below the lakes.

The flood wave gouged debris from the canyon bottom and sides that consisted mainly of an unconsolidated heterogeneous mass of earlier landslide deposits. It incorporated this debris, mixed with trees and vegetation that lined the canyon floor, into an increasingly abrasive mixture that gained momentum as it increased its mass during downstream transit. After about a mile, the channel gradient decreases to about 12 to 13 percent, but most of the material continued to move and the mass progressively increased as the bulldozing action persisted.

After about 8 minutes of travel, this high-momentum debris wave, with a leading edge about 30 feet in height, reached the canyon mouth where the channel abruptly widens and flattens. After traveling about 2.5 miles at an average velocity of 18 to 20 miles per hour, the boulder-laden flood wave destroyed two homes in its path.

It overtook four of five people racing to escape its wrath, killed one, and injured the other three. It continued across this road and downstream depositing large quantities of debris as the channel further expanded onto the fan, and the gradient rapidly decreased.

Maximum depth of fill across this road was about 9 feet. About 0.1 mile below the road, the moving mass destroyed one home and seriously damaged two others. Large boulder movement ceased just beyond this line of homes, but fine-grained, viscous run-out moved at least 0.2 mile farther to the edge of and onto U.S. 395, temporarily closing the southbound lanes. Fine-grained run-out continued to and along the west edge of the freeway for at least an hour. The mass movement of material from the slopes of Slide Mountain that began this disaster was probably triggered by increased hydraulic forces in the fractures and joints of the granodiorite bedrock. An abnormally high snowpack had been melting rapidly during several preceding days of above-normal air temperature (Glancy and others, 1984).

12.0 Ophir townsite historical marker on the right. Ophir sprang up in 1861 and reached a maximum population of 300 around 1862 or 1863. By 1871, only 41 residents remained.

About $^1/4$ mile to the east on U. S. 395 are the stone wall remnants of the Ophir mill, the largest ore-crushing mill in Washoe

Nevada Historical Society photo.

A remnant of stone wall is all that remains of the Ophir Mill in Washoe Valley (1974).

Valley, which processed gold and silver ore from the Ophir Mining Company's mine in Virginia City. It was erected in 1861 at a cost of $500,000, a lot of money in those days. Ore was hauled from Virginia City down the steep Ophir (Jumbo) Grade and across a mile-long wooden causeway built across the north end of Washoe Lake (see map on pages 54-55). The mill had 72 stamps, and could process up to 100 tons of ore per day. The mill closed in 1866, after the initial bonanza of rich ore of the Ophir mine had been exhausted. After that, it was more economical to mill the ore on the Carson River.

12.5 Davis Creek County Park on the left. This beautiful park offers day use and reserved camping sites, group picnic areas, hiking trails, and ice-skating in the winter.

13.0 Junction with new U.S. 395. Carefully turn left on U.S. 395 and continue north to Reno.

13.2 On the right is Theodore Winters' house built in 1861 with profits from the Comstock mines.

Theodore Winters was the first man to breed horses in Nevada. He was thorough, honest, and a good judge of men and horses. Many races were run here on his own racetrack—his most famous rival being prominent Virginia City attorney Charles Bryan.

Winters won most of the horse races he entered at the Bay District Racetrack in San Francisco, but the crowning event of his career was winning the American Derby in Chicago with his undefeated racer "Del Rio Rey," bred right here on his Washoe Valley ranch.

Winters was elected Territorial Representative in 1862. This house was the site of many social activities. At an 1864 Christmas party, Governor James Nye and Samuel Clemens (Mark Twain) were in attendance.

14.1 Entering old Washoe City.

Washoe City was founded in 1861 and became the county seat that same year. It soon became a major lumber- and ore-milling center for the Comstock mines. New mills built along the Carson River and the completion of the V & T Railroad from Carson City to Virginia City eliminated the need for the Comstock mines to use the difficult Ophir Grade to transport ore and lumber. By 1880, the population stood at around 200.

14.8 The stone building on the right is the former Washoe City jail. Just behind the building is the abandoned right-of-way of the V & T Railroad.

15.1 Crossing Steamboat Creek which flows north out of Little Washoe Lake through a deeply incised channel in Washoe Hill and continues

View looking southwest at Washoe City as it appeared in 1865.

north through Pleasant Valley, Steamboat Hot Springs, and the eastern margin of the Truckee Meadows to the Truckee River. The narrow gorge of Steamboat Creek, which is about 250 feet deep, is partial evidence indicating that the north end of Washoe Valley was tilted eastward in late Quaternary time after entrenchment of the outlet had started. The geologic history of this basin is complex. Along with tilting of the northern end of the basin, old gravels and faulted lacustrine deposits cap the surrounding hills. Erosion is destroying the connection between these isolated deposits. Washoe Valley has probably repeatedly contained larger lakes while Quaternary structural deformation competed with erosion and deposition (after Thompson and White, 1964).

The route ascends the south side of Washoe Hill. Little Washoe Lake is to the right. Four normal north-trending faults cross the road just before Eastlake Blvd.

15.5 Eastlake Blvd. on the right. The route now leaves Washoe Valley and descends into Pleasant Valley. The hills along both sides of the road are formed mainly of andesite breccias.

This area of abundant sagebrush and bitterbrush is winter habitat for the Sierra Nevada muledeer herd. Many artifacts have been found around the summit of Washoe Hill suggesting the early hunters concentrated their hunting activities along this natural game route.

16.5 The route now passes through the Galena mining district.

The Commonwealth mine (or Union mine), on the far left at 10:00 at the mouth of the canyon, was the original 1860 discovery site for the lead-silver ore in this area. Rocks surrounding the mine are metamorphosed sedimentary rocks intruded by Cretaceous granitic rocks. Other mines and prospects in this district dot the Steamboat Hills on the left and the Virginia Range on the right.

Successful mining in this district was short-lived. Lead-silver-zinc-copper ore worth $232,000 was mined during 1943-45, and minor amounts of ore were shipped at other periods.

16.9 Crossing Steamboat Creek. Boulder deposits at the edge of the fields on the left (about 10:00) are from the June 11, 1927 flood of Brown's Creek. A thunderstorm caused the dam on Grass Lake Reservoir (about 4.5 miles upstream) to fail.

Aerial view of Pleasant Valley looking southwest.

Ahead on the south slope of the Steamboat Hills, plumes of steam may usually be seen issuing from a geothermal plant.

17.7 Crossing Galena Creek.
Look ahead across the valley at the pastel colors of the altered rocks along the Geiger Grade.

18.7 The Victorian mansion on the left once belonged to Nevada Governor John Sparks (after whom the city of Sparks is named). It was relocated to its current site in 1988. The mansion originally stood at the intersection of Peckham Lane and South Virginia Street in Reno and was well known as Anderson Station and the Junction House and served as the last stopover on the Emigrant Trail over the Sierra. Sparks purchased the property in 1887 and renamed it the Alamo Ranch. He improved it considerably to include the state's first indoor heated swimming pool.

20.1 Buildings of a geothermal resort are on the right. A few homes in this area use geothermal energy for heating.

20.7 Steamboat Hot Springs lower terrace is on the left.

STEAMBOAT HOT SPRINGS

Steamboat Hot Springs is located in a shatter zone of north-trending faults (called the Steamboat Hot Springs fault system, part of the Sierra Nevada frontal fault zone) and is the site of frequent earthquake swarms probably related to tectonic processes. The vertical offset on the Steamboat Hot Springs fault system is at least 1,000 feet. (Refer to the map on page 20.)

The geothermal area occurs on a northeast-trending alignment of four rhyolite domes. (Refer to the map on page 27.) The domes erupted 3 to 1 million years ago (Pliocene and early Pleistocene) mantling much of the adjacent area with rhyolitic pumice. Springs were active 2.5 to 3 million years ago, prior to the eruption of the basaltic andesite of Steamboat Hills (consisting of flows and cinder cones), which is dated at 2.5 million years old. Hot springs deposits are present beneath some of these basalt flows. The High Terrace is about 30,000 years old.

The springs at Steamboat are near boiling, and temperatures as high as 442 °F have been recorded at depths over 3,000 feet. They most likely derive their heat from a rhyolitic intrusive body that lies deep under this area. Surface water seeps downward along the faults in this area, is heated, and rises back to the surface as steam and hot water. The deep geothermal fluids have a pH near 7 (neutral) and are high in sodium and chloride ions.

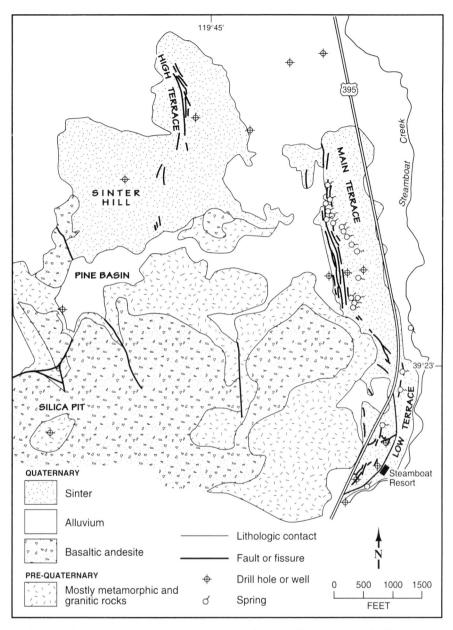

Geology of the Steamboat Hot Springs geothermal area (after Schoen and White, 1967).

As the heated groundwater rises, it boils and releases gases which combine with the condensed steam above the water table to form sulfuric acid. This process is dominant near the surface and above the water table where hydrogen sulfide rises and oxidizes to sulfuric acid by reaction with atmospheric oxygen and water. The rocks are said to have been affected

99

Aerial view looking northwest over the main terrace of Steamboat Hot Springs.
U.S. 395 is in the lower right.

by acid-sulfate alteration. The descending acidic water chemically leaches the rocks. Where the generation of acid has been abundant, the end result is replacement of the original silicate minerals (found in the original igneous rocks) by porous opal. See page 43 for a description of other geologic conditions under which acid sulfate rock alteration forms.

Recently deposited (younger) sinter consists mainly of opal which inverts to beta-cristobalite with increasing depth and age, and becomes chalcedony (without any opal) in the oldest sinter deposits. Chalcedonic sinter generally requires many thousands of years as well as temperatures near 260 °F for conversion from opaline sinter. The deposits of chalcedonic sinter are often colored pink by the presence of cinnabar (mercury sulfide) which turns black when exposed to sunlight. (This darkening is unusual and may be related to the fine grain size of the cinnabar.) Metastibnite is also present in the chalcedonic sinter.

Steamboat Hot Springs has the longest and most complex geologic history of any active geothermal system in the world, and has been studied since the 1880s. One phenomenon that generated interest in the hot springs was the presence of arsenic, mercury, antimony, gold, and silver. Sinter at the springs generally contains detectable amounts of gold and silver, and siliceous mud deposited in the spring pools contain as much as 10 ppm gold and nearly 40 ppm silver, along with 0.02 percent mercury and 3.9 percent antimony.

100

The Steamboat Hot Springs area serves as a modern analog for many hydrothermal ore deposits. The shallow boiling system has many of the features of epithermal and hot springs deposits found throughout the world. Study of this modern metal-depositing system can lead to a better understanding of and exploration for fossil hydrothermal systems (the Comstock Lode, for example).

In the 1850s the springs became a favorite camping ground for westward-bound travelers. By 1857, the name "Steamboat" (named for the puffing sight and sound of the escaping steam) was firmly affixed to the loosely knit assemblage of shanties, liveries, and crude hotels on the Virginia Road. From 1860 through 1890, with the discovery of the Comstock Lode, the opening of the Geiger-Tilton Toll Road, and the extension of the V & T Railroad to this point, a number of spas and resorts were developed at the hot springs.

In 1873, John Poe (the miner of Peavine Mountain fame and cousin to Edgar Allen Poe) and Louis Dean created the Nevada Quicksilver Mining

Area of acid sulfate alteration in Upper Pine Basin will only support Jeffrey pine.

101

Company. They erected a furnace in the "silica pit" and produced both mercury and sulfur for several years. Mining in the area has been sporadic for nearly 100 years since that time, with production totaling only about 100 flasks (about 7,600 pounds) of mercury.

The first deep test wells capable of production of geothermal fluids were drilled in 1979 and 1981 by Phillips Petroleum Company. Since the mid-1980s, several companies have been using the steam to generate electricity, which they sell to the local power company. As of this writing, the plants are capable of a combined production of about 48 megawatts of electricity.

21.2 Passing a power-generating geothermal plant on left.

21.9 Intersection of U.S. 395 and State Route 431 to Lake Tahoe and State Route 341 to Virginia City.

End of Trip B.

Steamboat Hot Springs in 1931.

Nevada Historical Society photo.

Trip C—Reno to Lake Tahoe to Carson City

This trip begins at Steamboat Hot Springs south of Reno and follows State Route 431 (the Mount Rose Highway) up to Incline Village on the northeast shore of Lake Tahoe. The route passes through several life zones and striking vegetation changes along the way. The high peaks are light-colored Cretaceous Sierran granodiorite capped with layers of darker Miocene andesite, a reminder of the recent geologic processes that formed the Tahoe basin and the surrounding mountains. Lake Tahoe—formed by the processes of fire and ice—is a jewel set among towering mountain peaks. The climate is wetter here than east of the Sierra Nevada because the mountains cause the moist air masses from the Pacific Ocean to drop their moisture in this area before moving eastward. The Tahoe area is closely linked historically to mining on the Comstock Lode over 100 years ago, and most of the trees in the basin were harvested in the 1860s to supply the Comstock mines and mills. Many immigrant trails passed through the south end of the basin to California. Today, the area is a major tourist destination; water sports, snow sports, and music and drama events occur throughout the year.

0.0 **Junction of U.S. 395 (south of Reno) and State Route 431 (Mount Rose highway). Turn right (west) onto State Route 431 and set odometer to 0.0.**

Steamboat Hot Springs geothermal area is on the left (refer to page 98 for a description of this area).

The route begins the climb up the huge, sloping Mount Rose fan and glacial outwash complex that extends eastward from the Carson Range (see the color photo on page 36). For the first mile or so from the intersection, the highway is built on outwash deposited by streams draining glaciers in the Carson Range during the oldest and most extensive of the three known periods of glaciation in the range. This material consists of a brown to gray sandy, muddy, poorly sorted, large-pebble gravel, with cobbles and small boulders common. Rock fragments found on the surface are dominantly volcanic. Granite fragments are rare. The deposits are deeply weathered and exhibit a strongly developed soil profile (after Bonham and Rogers, 1983). (See photo on page 29.)

The outwash becomes younger as the route proceeds uphill. For the next 4 miles, beginning at the Galena High School, the highway is built on outwash consisting mainly of granitic and volcanic rock

103

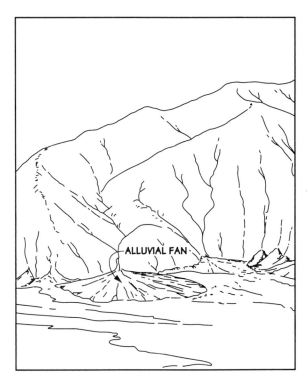

An alluvial fan, forming at the mouth of a canyon.

Age	Glaciation	
late Pleistocene	Tioga Till	Younger than Tahoe Till in Lake Tahoe area—separated by a significant interglaciation. Probably 10,000 to 20,000 years old.
middle Pleistocene	Tahoe Till and outwash	Probably 100,000 to 120,000 years old; may be somewhat younger. Glaciers caused a rise of Lake Tahoe of about 90 feet.
middle Pleistocene	Donner Lake Till and outwash	More extensive in Truckee area than Tahoe glaciation. Estimated to be older than 200,000 years. Glaciers caused Lake Tahoe to rise 600 feet. Large boulders common in Reno area outwash (from jokulhlaups).
early Pleistocene	Hobart Till	Correlated with the Sherwin Till of the southern Sierra Nevada. Probably about 800,000 to 900,000 years old. Much older than the Donner Lake Till.
late Pliocene	McGee Till	In southern Sierra Nevada. Probably about 2 million years old.

Generalized glacial history of the Lake Tahoe-Truckee area
(Birkeland, 1964, 1968; Fullerton, 1986).

fragments in a yellowish- to orange-brown, sandy, large-cobble to large-boulder gravel. These deposits have a strongly developed 3-foot thick soil profile. The different ages of the outwash are determined by the degree of development of soil horizons, composition and size of the rock fragments in the outwash, and the degree of weathering of the boulders and cobbles within the outwash.

The slope has been accentuated by the continued downward tilting of the eastern margin of the Truckee Meadows and the uplift of the Carson Range. This area is part of the Sierra Nevada frontal fault zone and has been highly faulted in Cenozoic time. The fault zone consists of broadly distributed mostly north-trending faults that form a series of subparallel grabens (German for "trenches"), or down-dropped areas, and has been called a "nested" graben complex.

0.8 The route crosses a fault controlled creek (fault trends north-south). Many of the creeks in this area are fault controlled.

1.5 The route crosses another north-trending fault having its down-dropped side on the west.

Carson Range segment of the Sierra Nevada frontal fault zone (after Ramelli, 1992).

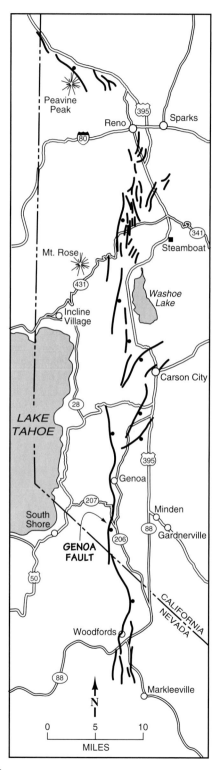

105

2.2 Lancer's Hill at 3:00 is composed of andesite flows. It is bounded on the east by a fault which is down-dropped to the east. Looking north (right), notice the numerous low swales and small hills of fault-controlled origin on the alluvial fan. Most of the west-facing embankments are fault scarps.

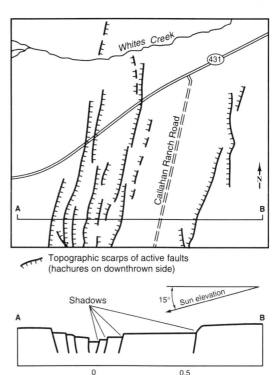

Topographic scarps of active faults (hachures on downthrown side)

North-south trending faults of the Carson frontal fault zone cutting Pleistocene alluvium in the Callahan Ranch Road area. These linear fault scarps are more apparent when observed or photographed from the air in the early morning or late afternoon when shadows along the scarps accentuate their visibility.

The northern Steamboat Hills on the left are composed of faulted andesite flows, with the underlying Cretaceous granodiorite exposed in the center of this northern section of the hills.

In the next 1.5 miles, the road crosses several fault scarps (down-dropped to the east) in outwash of the Mount Rose fan complex. These faults are evidence of very recent movement along faults in the underlying basement rock.

4.1 Callahan Ranch Road intersection. Houses in the development to the left are built around a large number of fault traces inferred to be Holocene age.

Straight ahead is the Carson Range. Gradual uplift of this region began around 90 million years ago. Erosion removed some of the overlying rock, and Tertiary volcanic rocks were laid down on this erosion surface. Erosion of these volcanic rocks in the late Tertiary followed uplift of the range associated with the basin-and-range faulting.

The current uplift of the Carson Range at this latitude began about 5 million years ago or less. Faulting, uplift, and volcanism around Lake Tahoe have progressed together from late Tertiary (Miocene-Pliocene) through Quaternary time. (See map on page 117).

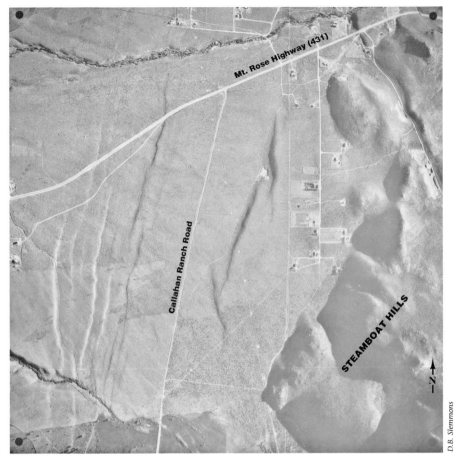

D.B. Slemmons

Aerial photo of the Mount Rose Highway and Callahan Ranch Road area taken in early morning. East-facing scarps are in bright sunlight and appear white; west-facing scarps are in shadows and appear dark.

The broad bowl of Mount Rose and its high U-shaped valleys were scoured by glaciers during the Pleistocene Epoch. Mount Rose appears darker than the other peaks in the Carson Range because it is topped with a layer of darker volcanic rocks of Miocene age.

5.5   Timberline Road intersection.

This area is in the Lower Transition life zone. Annual precipitation is 8 to 16 inches. Flora in this life zone include sagebrush, bitterbrush, desert peach, Mormon tea (ephedra), mountain mahogany, and many wildflowers and grasses. Fauna in this area include sagehen, black-billed magpie, pinyon jay, sage thrasher, various species of

107

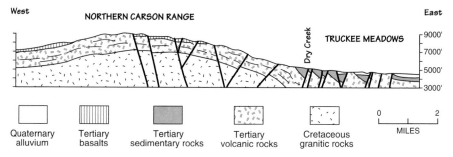

West   NORTHERN CARSON RANGE   East

Dry Creek   TRUCKEE MEADOWS

9000'
7000'
5000'
3000'

Quaternary alluvium	Tertiary basalts	Tertiary sedimentary rocks	Tertiary volcanic rocks	Cretaceous granitic rocks

0   2
MILES

Cross section of the Carson Range (after Thompson and White, 1964).

sparrow, jackrabbit, Nevada cottontail, pocket mice, kangaroo rats, and voles.

6.8 The route has just crossed a small section of andesite and has now entered the granodiorite of the Carson Range.

The vegetation has changed from sagebrush to the Upper Transition life zone which is characterized by ponderosa and Jeffrey pines, manzanita, tobacco brush, aspen, and many wildflowers. Annual precipitation is over 16 inches. Fauna include owls, woodpeckers, stellar jays, deer, chipmunks, and squirrels.

Characteristic vegetation of the mountain coniferous forest life zone.

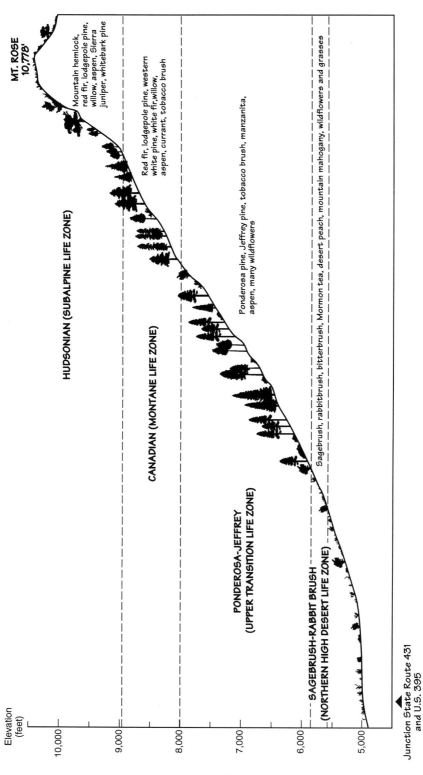

Elevation (feet)

MT. ROSE 10,778'

Mountain hemlock, red fir, lodgepole pine, willow, aspen, Sierra juniper, whitebark pine

Red fir, lodgepole pine, western white pine, white fir, willow, aspen, currant, tobacco brush

Ponderosa pine, Jeffrey pine, tobacco brush, manzanita, aspen, many wildflowers

Sagebrush, rabbitbrush, bitterbrush, Mormon tea, desert peach, mountain mahogany, wildflowers and grasses

HUDSONIAN (SUBALPINE LIFE ZONE)

CANADIAN (MONTANE LIFE ZONE)

PONDEROSA-JEFFREY (UPPER TRANSITION LIFE ZONE)

SAGEBRUSH-RABBIT BRUSH (NORTHERN HIGH DESERT LIFE ZONE)

Junction State Route 431 and U.S. 395

Life zones of the eastern slope of Mount Rose.

109

6.9 Galena Creek Park on the right. Enjoy the picnic facilities and great hiking trails. You can hike along streams all the way up to Mount Rose from here.

The headwaters of Galena Creek drain the east face of Mount Rose. Flash floods have occurred on this creek, mainly from November to January and in the midsummer months, since records began to be kept in the 1880s. Until 1943, Galena Creek had a fairly stable channel, but it has since been cut deep and wide due to the effects of fire, clear-cutting, and natural erosion. Several properties in the Galena Forest Estates subdivision are located within the historic flood zone.

8.6 The route passes through andesitic mudflow (lahar) deposits. They are recognized by their poorly stratified to unstratified (nonlayered) nature and the appearance of rounded to angular cobbles to pebbles of volcanic rock embedded in a mud-like matrix.

9.8 The route passes through thick shrubbery of manzanita, tobacco brush, and bitterbrush which followed a fire that burned stands of Jeffrey pine. Mountain mahogany and squawcarpet are also found here. Bitterbrush yields quality forage and provides good habitat for deer.

The soils are glacial in origin and composed of a deep mix of sand and boulders of various igneous rock types. A slight silica cementation produced within the soil profile during glaciation combined with southern exposure tend to slow growth and cause some stunting of the brush.

10.2 The Christmas Tree restaurant is on the left.

10.9 Mount Rose is directly ahead (elev. 10,778 feet). Note the dark mantle of andesite.

11.7 Passing Sky Tavern (ski facility of the Washoe County junior ski program) on the right.

12.0 Cretaceous granodiorite outcrops on the right.

12.2 Good views of Reno and Sparks in the Truckee Meadows to the left.

12.9 Good view to the southeast of Pleasant and Washoe Valleys with the Virginia Range on the skyline. Virginia City is behind Mount Davidson (the highest peak in the range).

13.1 The road to Slide Mountain portion of the Mount Rose Ski Area is just ahead on the left. Slide Mountain (elev. 9,698 feet) is composed

Mount Rose looking northwest.

entirely of light-colored Cretaceous granodiorite. Note the snow avalanche chutes on the side of the mountain to the south.

This is an excellent place to observe a variety of vegetation types of the Canadian (montane) life zone. Red fir, lodgepole pine, and western white pine create a dense forest growth. Along the stream (riparian zone) willow, aspen, alder, currant, and lupine are a few of the dominant plant types.

14.0 The entrance to the Mount Rose Ski Resort is on the left.

15.1 On the left, the route passes a typical cross section of glacial moraine material.

15.3 A small subalpine meadow is on the left.

16.0 Note the well-developed joints (irregular fractures) in granodiorite on the right. These joints probably developed as a result of the release of residual stress as these rocks were uplifted from the considerable depth where they crystallized from magma to their present site at the Earth's surface.

111

Vegetation typical of the Canadian life zone.

16.4 Mount Rose Summit (elev. 8,933 feet). This is actually a pass through the Carson Range. Mountain hemlock, red fir, lodgepole pine, willow, aspen, Sierra juniper, and whitebark pine are now evident in the vegetation characteristic of the Hudsonian (subalpine) life zone.

Note the historical marker on the east side of the road. Mount Rose was probably named for Jacob Rose, a rancher in the area in the 1850s. The summit was the site of America's first high altitude weather observatory. Dr. James Church, Jr., a professor of classics at the University of Nevada from 1890 to 1939, established the observatory in 1905. He conducted year-round snow studies and was the founder of the modern science and technique of snow survey, which is used throughout the world today to predict seasonal water flow from precipitation stored in the form of snow. Winds and blizzards near the peak present some of the most extreme climatic conditions found anywhere in the world.

Whitebark pine on Mt. Rose

16.5 Mount Rose campground is to the left via the small road through the trees, and Lake Tahoe and the Sierra Nevada crest are straight ahead. "Sierra Nevada" is Spanish for "snowy mountain range." The Sierra Nevada forms an uplifted block of the earth's crust roughly 50 miles wide and more than 400 miles long; uplift continues today. The granitic rock that forms the core of the range began to form over 180 million years ago as magma deep within the boundary between oceanic crust and continental crust; the magma rose very slowly as giant teardrop-shaped bodies and cooled to form the plutons of the main Sierra Nevada. More recently, faulting has uplifted the Sierran block while erosion has worn away most of the overlying rock to expose the granite. (Refer to page 13 for more information on the formation of the Sierra Nevada through time).

16.8 The trailhead to Mount Rose summit is on the right (the dirt road just west of the small building).

17.1 Interpretive Center and restrooms on the left at the head of Tahoe Meadows. This is the trailhead for hiking down Slide Mountain past Upper Price and Lower Price Lakes to Davis Creek County Park on Franktown Road (refer to page 95).

18.1 Entering the Lake Tahoe basin.

18.7 Incline Lake can be seen through the trees to the right. This lake was created by a small glacier that descended out of Ginny Lake basin located to the northwest. The glacier terminated just downstream from here.

19.6 Scenic overlook on the right.

20.9 The Diamond Peak Ski Area is on the left.

21.0 **Scenic overlook on the left. Carefully pull off for a view of Lake Tahoe.**

LAKE TAHOE

Formed by a combination of shattering earthquakes, molten lava, and glacial ice, Lake Tahoe occupies a valley between the main crest of the Sierra Nevada and the Carson Range (see aerial color photo on page 36). It is about 22 miles long and 12 miles wide. The average depth of the water is 1,000 feet. The greatest measured depth is 1,645 feet. The maximum elevation of the lake surface, as mandated by court decree, is 6,229.1 feet above mean sea level and is controlled by a dam at the outlet.

Lake Tahoe is commonly included in the Sierra Nevada geomorphic province; however, its formation is due to basin-and-range faulting and volcanism. The granitic rocks of the Sierra Nevada extend eastward to the Carson Valley, while the structure of the Basin and Range province extends westward to the west side of the lake. The Tahoe basin is a down-dropped block (graben), boxlike in shape, and bordered by steeply dipping faults between the two range crests. The floor of the basin at the lake bottom is 4,700 feet above sea level, about the same elevation as the surface of Carson Valley to the east.

The Sierra Nevada block began to be faulted upward and tilted to the west about 6 million years ago. Faulting, volcanism, and uplift around the lake have progressed together from the late Tertiary (Miocene-Pliocene time) through the Quaternary. The lake basin was formed by faulting and volcanism probably beginning about 5 million years ago. Continued faulting, as well as volcanism, have maintained the lake basin during the last 2 million years or so.

Studies of Miocene-Pliocene fossil plants in western Nevada and in eastern California by Axelrod (1957, 1962, and 1992) and Axelrod and Ting (1960) indicate a similar climate for both areas and a maximum elevation at that time of 2,000 to 3,000 feet. He suggested, therefore, that the Sierran block has been uplifted in this area 5,000 to 6,500 feet, relative to the surrounding region, since early Pliocene time. Boundary faults for Lake Tahoe have been largely obscured by the more recent volcanic flows and glacial deposits; however, portions of the faults or fault zones can be traced in a number of areas surrounding the lake.

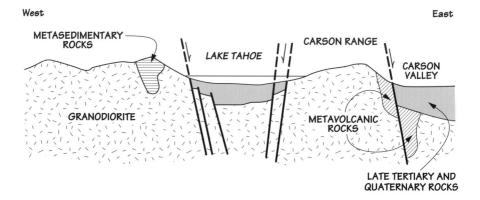

Diagrammatic cross section across the Sierra Nevada to Carson Valley
(modified from Brice, 1960).

114

There are four major groups of rocks present in the Lake Tahoe basin: (1) pre-Cretaceous metamorphic rocks, (2) Jurassic and Cretaceous granitic plutonic (intrusive) rocks of the Sierra Nevada batholith, (3) Tertiary (Miocene and Pliocene) and Quaternary (Pleistocene) volcanic rocks, and (4) Quaternary glacial and fluvial deposits.

The pre-Cretaceous rocks are metamorphosed sedimentary or volcanic rocks that occur as masses (roof pendants) surrounded by granitic rocks of the Sierra Nevada batholith. They are exposed on the western and southwestern sides of the lake basin. A good example of a roof pendant is Mount Tallac.

The Sierra Nevada is 400 miles long and 50 to 60 miles wide. It extends from the Mojave Desert in southern California to the Cascade Range on the north. The batholith is a composite of hundreds of plutons (intrusive igneous rock bodies), mostly Jurassic and Cretaceous granodiorite. These plutons were, to some extent, the magma chambers of volcanoes that have long since eroded away.

Extensive Tertiary and Quaternary volcanic rocks cover large areas in the northwestern part of the Tahoe basin and immediately outside the basin on the north and south. These volcanic rocks consist of mudflows and flows of basalt and andesite. The mudflows (lahars) are crudely stratified, massive, thick-bedded, and well- to loosely consolidated. Lahars can form by a number of processes related to composite volcano development. These include volcanic eruptions in crater lakes and subsequent mudflows, debris flows from areas of oversteepened ash and lava blocks during torrential rains, and volcanic (including pyroclastic) eruptions in volcano snowfields. These lahars can be either hot or cold, and may flow tens of miles over gentle slopes to eventually accumulate to great thicknesses. Most of the more extensive landslide areas in the northern part of the basin are formed in these mudflow rocks.

The andesite and basalt flows are more thinly layered than the lahars and display prominent joints. They are more resistant to weathering than the mudflows, and support only a thin veneer of soil. Because water freely penetrates the joints, talus slopes form below these flows as a result of mechanical weathering (freezing and thawing, for example).

Most of the major landforms that we see today in the Lake Tahoe area formed by faulting and warping after the major period of andesitic volcanism and lahar deposition (thus, mainly in the last 10 million years). The Lake Tahoe basin formed by faulting. It is bounded on its east and west sides by north-trending faults which form the margins of the graben, and have scarps of 5,000 to 6,000 feet. The north end is also probably fault-bounded by a scarp of 1,200 to 1,400 feet.

The first glaciation in the Sierra Nevada probably began about 1.5 million years ago. During the Pleistocene Epoch, ice covered all but the highest peaks and ridges of the Sierra Nevada west of Lake Tahoe. Glaciers, almost 1,000 feet thick at their maximum, moved eastward down the canyons scouring loose rock and piling it up into lateral, medial, and terminal

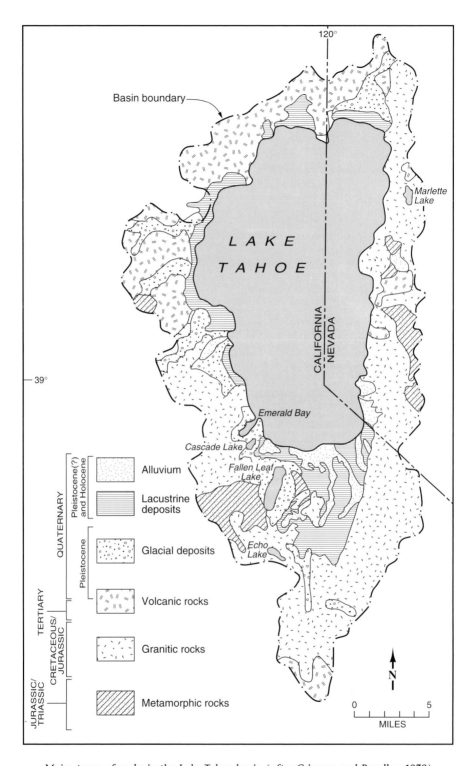

Major types of rocks in the Lake Tahoe basin (after Crippen and Pavelka, 1970).

116

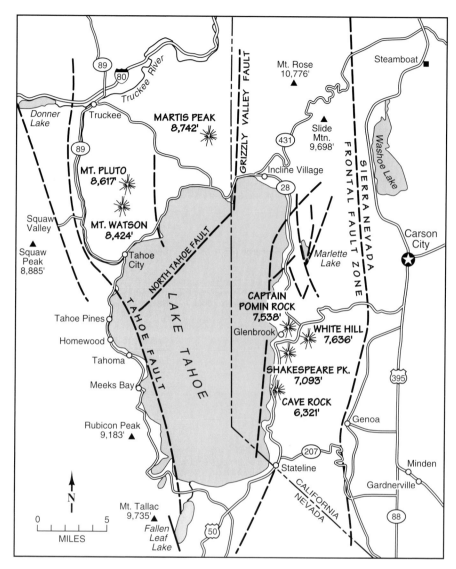

*Main fault zones and eruptive centers around the Lake Tahoe basin
(Burnett, 1971; Grose, 1985, 1986; Saucedo and Wagner, 1992).*

moraines (the small lakes southwest of Lake Tahoe are dammed, in part, by glacial moraines).

On the eastern side of the basin, in the Carson Range, only the northern exposures of the highest peaks developed glaciers (small moraines can be found on the eastern slopes of Mount Rose near Galena Creek). With the highest elevation in both ranges being equal, the difference in glaciation was directly related to the different amounts of snowfall each side of the

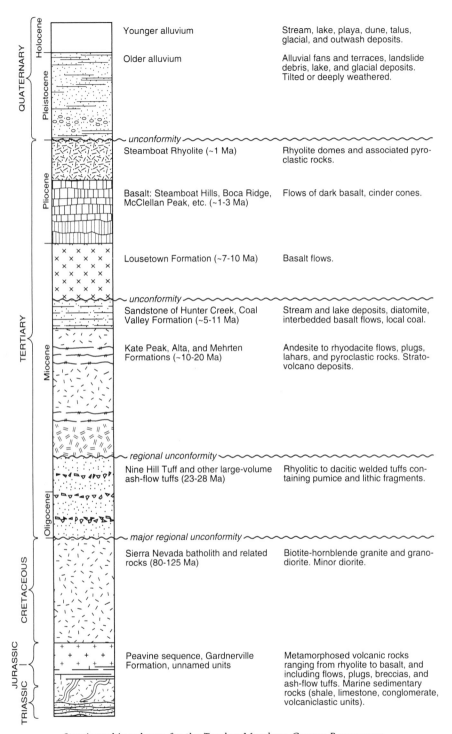

Stratigraphic column for the Truckee Meadows-Carson Range area.

basin received. The rugged topography of the area west of the lake is a result of scouring by glaciers.

Then, as now, the weather systems came mostly from the west and the annual precipitation decreased from west to east across the basin. The average annual precipitation on the western Sierra Nevada crest is up to 90 inches, but it is little more than 40 inches on the highest peaks in the Carson Range.

Clues derived from relating dated volcanic rocks and landforms to associated glacial deposits, mapping fluctuations in timberline with tree ring measurements and carbon-14 dating, and dating volcanic ash in soil horizons show that the Sierra Nevada harbored glaciers at least 2 million years ago. In the Lake Tahoe area glacial activity having the most remaining features is at least 200,000 years old. Glacial advances are also believed to have occurred at least three more times since then (at 100,000 to 120,000 years, at 20,000 years, and 10,000 years ago).

The glacial history in this area is also indicated by isolated patches of lacustrine deposits and strandlines (former shorelines) that can be found at elevations of 6,800 feet around Lake Tahoe. These deposits were laid down when the lake level was up to 600 feet higher than it is today. Rises in lake level were due to the formation of ice dams at the outlet to the headwaters of the Truckee River.

Because the density of ice is 9/10 that of water, an ice dam will tend to float when the water level behind it reaches 9/10 of its height. At this point, catastrophic floods of water are released along the base of the ice. "Jokulhlaup" is the Icelandic term applied to such glacial outburst floods. Evidence of these prehistoric floods is found high on the walls of the Truckee River canyon from Tahoe City downstream to Verdi. Huge granodiorite boulders found in the Tahoe outwash and floodplain deposits from Reno to Mustang are also attributed to these episodes of flooding.

Much of the ice last melted about 10,000 years ago, but since then, the climate has cooled enough at least twice that small glaciers formed in the Sierra Nevada. These cool periods were around 1410 A.D. and from 1700 to 1750 A.D.

The Lake Tahoe area was part of the summer range of the Washoe Indians. They sought the cooler temperatures in the summer months and, being mobile people, lived in brush and bark dwellings at several sites. Basketry was highly developed (there was almost no pottery) and was used for many purposes, including cooking. Their diet was limited but plentiful in season: pinyon nuts, grasshoppers, caterpillars, larvae, fish, lizards, birds, plant bulbs, berries, and an occasional deer.

Numerous sites of Washoe villages have been found around the lake shore. They are marked by circles of rocks and by holes worn in rock outcrops from grinding nuts.

John C. Frémont and Charles Preuss of the U.S. Topographical Engineers climbed Red Lake Peak south of the basin near Carson Pass on February 14, 1844 and had the first recorded look at Lake Tahoe: "We had a beautiful

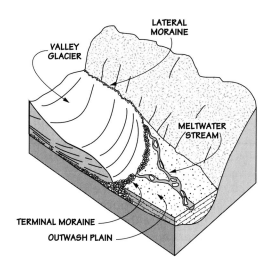

Landforms developed by valley glaciation (after Hamblin, 1975).

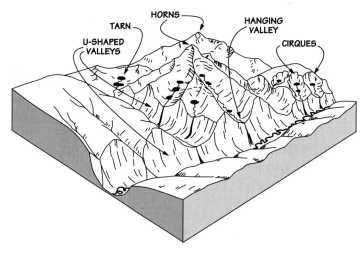

view of a mountain lake at our feet, about 15 miles in length, and so entirely surrounded by mountains that we could not discover an outlet."

Frémont named the lake "Bonpland" after the French naturalist. It was also named "Bigler" (after a California governor) in 1869 but the Indians had already established their own name, "Ta-hoe-hee," for the lake. "Ta" is the Washoe root for "water," and "tah-oo" or "ta-au" means "lake water" or "sheet of water."

By the early 1860s Glenbrook, located on the southeast shore of the lake, had become a celebrated resort in the Tahoe basin. By 1905, cars were making the trip here from Sacramento in 8 hours. Lots were being sold on the north shore in 1911, and by 1927 subdividing around the lake was commencing in earnest. By the end of World War II, there were still only about 1,000 permanent residents around the lake, but by the late 1940s growth began to mushroom. Skiing, gambling, and resort hotels helped draw a new generation to this area.

21.7 Roadcuts on the right for the next few miles are in andesite, which has been stabilized using gabions.

24.4 Crossing Second Creek. In August 1967, a mudflow washed down this creek destroying the only home in the area at that time. Now, many homes occupy the area, but no precautions have been taken for future mudslides.

Sugar pine trees are directly ahead at the stop sign. They produce cones up to 18 inches long.

24.6 **Junction. State Route 431 ends. Turn left on State Route 28.**

24.9 Entering Incline Village. Most of the town is built on steep unstable slopes of weathered granodiorite or andesite, on old Lake Tahoe shoreline sediments, or on alluvium washed down from the Mount Rose area to the northeast.

Incline Village began as a settlement around 1879 when the Sierra Nevada Wood and Lumber Company erected a sawmill. By 1881, a narrow-gauge railroad was hauling timber to this mill. Logging ceased here in 1895 and the town has become a tourist center.

25.7 Village Blvd. intersection.

26.6 Country Club Drive intersection.

27.3 Entrance to Ponderosa Ranch, a western village with a replica of the "Bonanza" TV series ranch house. Note the historical marker on the left.

Note the trace of the "incline" (from which this town received its name) up the mountain behind the Ponderosa Ranch. This 4,000-foot-long tramway carried lumber 1,400 vertical feet up to V-shaped flumes which transported it down the east side of the Carson Range.

By 1861, the logging industry had begun to establish itself in the basin. Much of the virgin timber met its fate to provide lumber and fuel for the mines and mills of the Comstock Lode. The majestic Jeffrey pine, ponderosa pine, and sugar pine (known as the "queen of the Sierra") were particularly prized for lumber. Timber was

121

The "incline" at Incline Village which led up to Spooner Meadow.

R.J. Waters photo.

transported to millsites around the lake by steamers. Inclines, small railroads, and oxen pulling wagons hauled the timber to the passes in the Carson Range to be transported by water flumes down various canyons to sawmills in Washoe Valley and Carson City. A few traces of these flumes remain today.

27.7 Lake Shore Drive intersection.

30.2 Entrance to Sand Harbor boat ramp.

30.3 Entrance to Sand Harbor State Park ahead on the right. This park has one of the finest beaches around Lake Tahoe. The water is shallow for quite a distance out into the protected bay. There are good restroom and shower facilities, and beautiful picnic areas in stands of tall Jeffrey pines. North of the swimming beach is another embayment where boats may be launched.

    This area was also a site of logging operations during the late 19th and early 20th centuries. A log loader, steam plant, and a narrow-gauge railway were all situated here. Walter Hobart, a Tahoe logging baron, owned the land and built a home near here in the 1920s after logging operations ceased. Sand Point is ahead on the right.

31.7 Exfoliation of granite on the left side of the road. **Carefully turn off to the right.**

    Where the knobs of granodiorite have not been fractured, they are more resistant to erosion. In this situation, the rock will spall off or split away in scale-like layers (like an onion) from an exposed or soil-covered surface of massive rock. This process is called exfoliation.

View of Sand Harbor State Park beach from the road.

Exfoliation of granitic rock in the Sierra Nevada.

32.8 Leaving Washoe County. Entering Carson City Rural Area.

32.9 U.S. Forest Service rest area with interpretive sign on the right.

33.8 Carefully turn off to the right on to paved turnout to observe spheroidal weathering in granodiorite on the left side of the road.

Spheroidal weathering in granitic rocks occurs as water enters joints in the rock and chemically and mechanically attacks the individual mineral grains, causing the rock to disintegrate. Where two or more sets of joint fractures intersect at nearly right angles, rounded masses of fresh, unweathered granodiorite are eventually left, surrounded by a square pattern of deeply weathered, crumbly rock material (representing the original square pattern of the joints).

On the eastern, less glaciated side of the basin, the granodiorite has been most affected by the combined action of water, atmospheric gases, and organic acids from decaying plant material.

Most of the minerals that make up the granitic rock are not chemically stable in the zone of weathering at or near the surface of the earth. The biotite is altered first by hydrolysis by rainwater and organic (carbonic) acids from decaying vegetation. These solutions creep into minute fractures in the rock, altering the biotite to chlorite, a slightly expanded mineral. This expansion shatters the surrounding mineral grains allowing more water to enter the rock (Wahrhaftig and others, 1965). The weak acid solutions also leach the calcium, potassium, and sodium out of the feldspar, altering it to clay. The relatively stable quartz and hornblende grains are left uncemented and, eventually, the once solid granite is reduced to loose piles of coarse granite sand called grus.

34.7 The road crosses a northeast-trending fault and parallels it for the next 0.3 mile. The southeast side has been dropped down and is marked by meadows and ponds along the fault trace.

35.9 Pray Meadows (named for Captain Augustus W. Pray who built the first sawmill in Glenbrook) is below the road on the right. The former Glenbrook logging railroad stretched north from Glenbrook through Pray Meadows and then up steep switchbacks to Spooner Summit ahead. The old zigzagging roadbed is still in evidence, as are areas where trestles were built.

36.6 Leaving Carson City Rural Area. Entering Douglas County.

Spheroidal weathering in granitic rock.

125

Nevada Bureau of Mines and Geology photo.

Logging operations in the Carson Range in the 1870s.

Nevada Bureau of Mines and Geology photo.

Lumber transfer yard and flume at Spooner Summit in the 1870s.

37.0 The route leaves granodiorite and quartz monzonite here and enters into Jurassic(?) metamorphosed volcanic rocks.

Spooner Meadows are ahead on the left. The former Glenbrook narrow-gauge logging railroad passed through the south part of these meadows toward the Spooner Summit flume.

37.3 Entrance to Spooner Lake State Park is on the left. The route now crosses into Miocene volcanic rocks.

A 4-mile hiking trail begins at the southwest edge of Spooner Lake and ends at Marlette Lake, the main source of water for Virginia City since 1873. (Refer to page 85 for the story of the Comstock water supply.)

Aerial view of Marlette Lake, looking north. Marlette Lake is in a fault-bounded basin, probably similar to the Lake Tahoe basin on the left.

Spooner Lake will be visible just ahead on the left. It has been made deeper by a small earthen dam on the west end.

37.9 **Keep to the right at Spooner Junction to enter U.S. 50 South** toward South Lake Tahoe.

38.4 In the next mile the route passes through a sequence of Mesozoic hydrothermally altered multicolored granitic and volcanic rocks.

In the Tahoe basin, Jeffrey pine and white fir have experienced much stress from drought in recent years; nearly one-third of the trees died in the early 1990s. Drought stress is caused

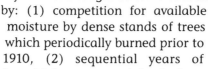

White fir

by: (1) competition for available moisture by dense stands of trees which periodically burned prior to 1910, (2) sequential years of

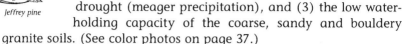

Jeffrey pine

drought (meager precipitation), and (3) the low water-holding capacity of the coarse, sandy and bouldery granite soils. (See color photos on page 37.)

The weakened trees have been unsuccessful in fighting off bark beetles. Normally, a beetle will bore through the bark, but will then be expelled by a healthy tree's defensive habit of encasing the insect in pitch. A weakened tree becomes infested with beetles that girdle the cambium and eat the storage tissue of the tree. They also carry into the tree a blue fungus that blocks the tree's water transportation system—keeping the sap from flowing. A large tree can house several hundred thousand beetles. Eventually, the tree dies.

Bark beetle larva
and adult

39.9 A northwest-trending fault crosses the road here where the altered granitic rock meets dark hornblende diorite (look left).

The prominent peak of dark rocks ahead is Shakespeare Point. It is part of a volcanic neck.

Shakespeare Point.

40.4 Glenbrook turnoff is on the right. Glenbrook was the first permanent settlement at Lake Tahoe and the focal point for the logging industry in the late 19th century. Captain A.W. Pray built a sawmill here in 1861. It became an industrial area of logging camps, sawmills, railroads, barges, and flumes—all to provide timber for the mines of Virginia City. Production reached a record high in 1875, but, by the late 1880s logging and milling in the area had essentially died out in direct correlation with the rise and fall of mining on the Comstock. Today, decaying pier pilings in the bay remain as evidence of past logging operations.

Two famous hotels, the Glenbrook House and the Lakeshore Hotel, offered complete resort accommodations for the wealthy folk who came to visit this celebrated vacation destination beginning in the early 1860s.

42.1 **Logan Shoals Vista Point on the right**. Logan Shoals are just beyond the beach area.

42.9 Cave Rock, directly ahead, is an eroded Miocene volcanic neck similar to Shakespeare Point. During the Pleistocene, the lake level was 140 feet higher and caves were cut high on the south side of the rock by wave action.

43.3 Cave Rock boat landing on the right. As at Incline Village, subdivisions have been constructed here on extremely steep terrain of unstable decomposing granodiorite and quartz monzonite. Natural stream channels have been straightened and confined. Development of meadowlands along the lake shore has disturbed the low-velocity, settling-basin effect of the marshes. Rather than being filtered out, silt and sand particles now wash directly into Lake Tahoe, diminishing clarity of the water. The rate of sedimentation in the lake basin in the last 30 years (due to urban growth) is equal to the sedimentation that occurred during the clear-cut logging days of the late 19th century when 60 percent of the basin's timber was removed for mining needs in Virginia City (Reno Gazette-Journal, 1995).

Between 1968 and 1995, Lake Tahoe's clarity—the depth one can see down into the lake—has declined 31 percent, from 102 feet to 70.5 feet, an average of more than a foot a year. Growth of algae is the main reason for this clouding of the water. Pollutants such as nitrogen and phosphorus fertilizers which originate from urban runoff, soil erosion (decaying vegetation), air pollution (mainly auto emissions), and other sources provide nourishment for the algae.

45.9 Zephyr Cove is to the right. It is built on granitic sand and gravel washed down from the local streams to the left.

47.0 Marla Bay is on the right.

47.6 Round Mound (elev. 6,720 feet), ahead, is a resistant knob of Cretaceous granodiorite.

48.2 Intersection with Elks Point Road. Elk Beach is on the right.

48.6 Note the meadow area on the right formed on decomposed granodiorite sands eroded from the Carson Range on the left.

   At 1:00 is the city of South Lake Tahoe. The large casinos end a short distance beyond at the California state line.

49.5 **Junction of U.S. 50 and State Route 207 (Kingsbury Grade).**

0.0 **Turn left onto State Route 207 and reset odometer to 0.0.**

   This road follows the original Daggett Trail to Daggett Pass (ahead) established around 1850. It stretched from Genoa on the east side of the Carson Range to Georgetown in the Mother Lode country of California.

2.1 Good exposures of granodiorite weathering along joint fractures on the left.

Meadows encroached upon by the city of South Lake Tahoe.
Part of the Heavenly Valley Ski Resort is on the left slope.

Granodiorite weathering along joint fractures in the Kingsbury Grade area.

2.9 Daggett Summit (elev. 7,334 feet). This pass and the trail through it were named for Dr. Charles D. Daggett in 1854, an early settler who laid claim to a sizable acreage along the route.

From here down to the floor of Carson Valley to the east, the route follows the new Kingsbury Grade. The original Kingsbury Grade toll road (up Haines Canyon) was constructed on this portion of the Daggett Trail from 1858 through 1860 by David D. Kingsbury and John McDonald. It was then used by the Overland Stage Line and the Pony Express. The original route is intersected several times by this new road on its descent to the valley.

3.9 Light-colored pegmatite and granodiorite intrude darker granodiorite on the left.

5.3 The Carson Valley is ahead.

6.4 On the left, note the 4,000-foot vertical escarpment of the Sierra Nevada frontal fault zone, which is locally called the Genoa fault. The vertical offset across this fault is almost 8,000 feet (see color photo on page 38).

Heavenly Valley Ski Resort is on the left skyline.

Light-colored pegmatite and granodiorite intrude darker granodiorite.

8.1 Look north (left) at the original Kingsbury Grade and the sharp angle the Genoa fault scarp makes with the lower part of the mountain front.

To the right, Carson Valley is bounded on the west by the Carson Range (composed mostly of Cretaceous granodiorite) and on the east by the Pine Nut Mountains (composed of Mesozoic through Tertiary granite, metamorphosed sedimentary rocks, and sedimentary and volcanic rocks). The structural block underlying this valley tilts to the west. Evidence for this tilting can be seen ahead near Genoa.

Like the Truckee Meadows and Washoe and Eagle Valleys to the north, Carson Valley is in the rain-shadow of the Sierra Nevada. The west side of the valley is wetter than the east side. Carson Valley is crossed by the East and West Forks of the Carson River—high-quality water that flows northeastward into the Carson Sink near Fallon.

10.9 Intersection with State Route 206. Turn left onto State Route 206 to Genoa.

Route 206 follows the old Emigrant trail (active from 1846 to 1870), the Overland Stage, and the Pony Express (active from 1860 to 1861) routes along the western edge of the Carson Valley north to Carson City. The Pony Express days ended due to the completion of the Overland Telegraph, the financial collapse of the promoters, and the start of the Civil War (see the map on page 17).

11.6 Along the base of the hill to the left, a series of riparian areas of aspen and poplar mark the trace of the Genoa fault. The Genoa fault is the principal fault trace of the northern Sierra Nevada fault zone in this area. It extends from Jobs Canyon on the south to Jacks Valley, where a second set of Holocene faults branch eastward to Carson City.

13.6 The foot of the original Kingsbury Grade and a historical marker on the left.

14.0 Junction. Road to the right connects with U.S. 395. Continue straight ahead.

14.1 Van Sickle Station on the left. The Genoa fault surface is exposed on the left. Slickensides can be observed in the granodiorite gouge. The dark rocks are Mesozoic metamorphosed volcanic rocks. Note the lush vegetation fed by springs issuing along the fault.

14.6 Walley's Hot Springs on the right. The resort features hot mineral pools, saunas, freshwater swimming pool, and workout room. The cold and hot springs observed issuing from along the margin of the Carson Range are directly related to the range-front fault.

Springs and riparian areas along the Genoa fault.

Good exposure of the slickensides of the Genoa fault in a gravel pit just south of Genoa.

David and Harriet Walley established an elaborate spa here in 1862, adjacent to the Emigrant Trail. Such historic figures as President U.S. Grant, Mark Twain, and Clark Gable visited here. During prohibition, Walley's became a famous bootlegger hangout and was the alleged hiding place of "Baby Face" Nelson in the 1930s. Buildings have been rebuilt several times on the site, now a modern destination resort.

15.0 The slickensides on polished granite which mark the actual fault plane of the Genoa fault are spectacularly exposed in the decomposed granite borrow pit on the left.

Detailed examinations of cross sections of the alluvial terraces nearby indicate that several seismic events (earthquakes) formed this scarp. Geologic studies by Pease (1979) indicate that both splays are less than several thousand years old. The Genoa fault scarp is geomorphically very young, and may be less than a few hundred years old. Historical records indicate that it formed prior to 1854 (Lawson, 1912; Bell, 1981). See the map on page 105.

The most recent fault displacements have produced triangular facets on the range front, and a youthful-appearing fault scarp with a vertical displacement of about 34 feet and a slope of about 38 degrees (after Slemmons, 1975).

15.5 Note the marshy area on the right. The Carson River flows quite close to the base of the Carson Range through an extensive marsh, indicating that the valley floor has been tilted (down-thrown) to the west during earthquake movements along the Genoa fault.

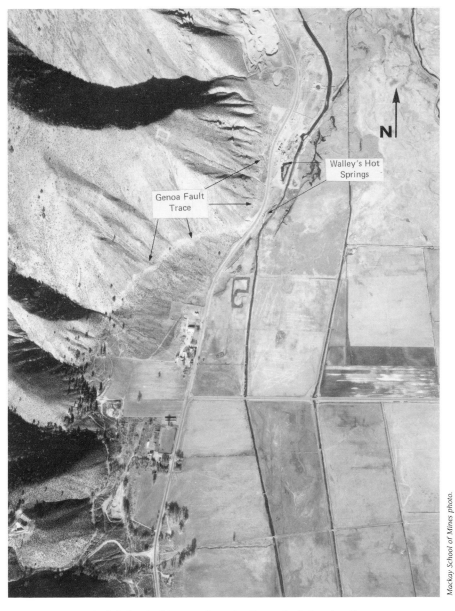

Mackay School of Mines photo.

Aerial view looking north at the Genoa fault forming the eastern base of the Carson Range.

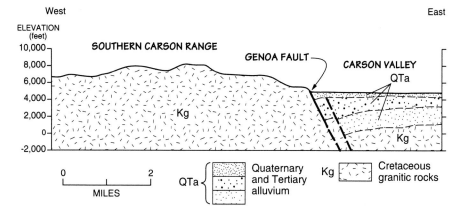

West   East

ELEVATION
(feet)
10,000 —   SOUTHERN CARSON RANGE
8,000 —   GENOA FAULT
6,000 —   CARSON VALLEY
4,000 —   QTa
2,000 —   Kg
0 —
-2,000 —   Kg

0   2
|_____| QTa   Quaternary   Kg   Cretaceous
  MILES   and Tertiary   granitic rocks
                         alluvium

Schematic cross section of the Genoa fault (after Ramelli, 1992).

16.2 The route crosses Genoa Canyon, an area of high flood and debris flow hazard. A debris flow crossed the road here in 1971.

16.3 Entering Genoa, Nevada's oldest settlement. Take time to visit the courthouse, Mormon Station State Park, and the Historical Society Museum.

Genoa was a camping spot on the California Emigrant Trail in 1848 and 1849. In 1850, when Congress designated this portion of the Great Basin as part of Utah Territory and Brigham Young was appointed Territorial Governor, a stockade and a corral were built by the stream and Mormons began a trading station. Here immigrants were able to obtain clothing and supplies. The surrounding land was cultivated with wheat, barley, corn, melons, turnips, and other vegetables. Emigrant travel was heavy during 1852, and a permanent settlement began to grow around the trading post. A crude government was established to handle land titles, laws, and regulations (after Paher, 1970).

Being an outpost of the Mormon Church, the town took the name of Mormon Station. It became the seat of Carson County, Utah Territory in 1854. The name was changed to Genoa in 1855, after the birthplace of Christopher Columbus, and a townsite was laid out. In 1857, when a dispute over its policies arose between the church and the U.S. Government, Brigham Young ordered all Mormon settlers in the region along the base of the Carson Range to return to Salt Lake City. They were forced to abandon their homes or accept very low payment for them.

Genoa grew with the development of the Comstock mines. The *Territorial Enterprise* was established here in 1858, before being moved to Carson City, and then on to Virginia City. In 1910, half of the business district of the town was burned down, including the courthouse and the original Mormon fort.

17.8   The tall, dark green shrubs on the slopes on the left are bitterbrush, which is excellent forage for deer.

19.5   Look to the left for another excellent view of the fresh-looking Genoa fault scarp at the base of the Carson Range. This scarp is up to 40 feet high in this area. The fault itself dips eastward about 60 degrees. The

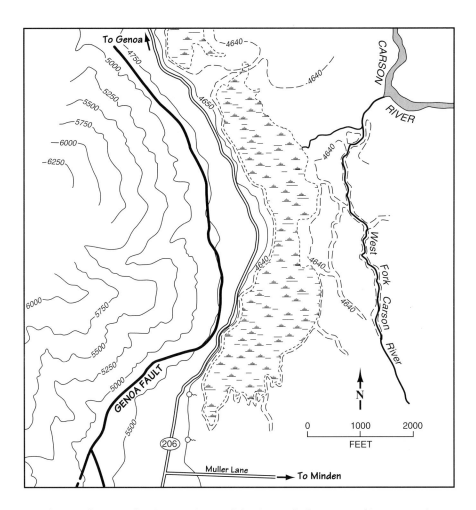

Marshy area between the Carson River and the Genoa fault, topographic contours in feet above sea level (modified from Ramelli, 1992).

Bitterbrush (Purshia tridentata).

two most recent fault movements occurred about 500 to 650 and 2,100 to 2,300 years ago. The Genoa fault terminates in this area and the Carson Range segment of the Sierra Nevada frontal fault zone continues north through Carson City.

Vertical offset of the rocks along the Sierra Nevada frontal fault zone in the Jacks Valley area is as much as 8,000 feet, with an accompanying north-trending vertical escarpment of 4,000 feet.

20.1 Hobo Hot Springs geothermal area is on the right at the southwestern edge of the small hill. The springs discharge 114 °F water at the rate of 1 to 15 gallons per minute.

20.5 The route leaves the Carson Valley and enters smaller Jacks Valley.

23.5 The scarp of the Carson Range frontal fault is on the left.

24.5 The route begins climbing Indian Hill which separates Carson Valley from Eagle Valley.

25.2 Junction with U.S. 395. Turn left onto U.S. 395.

26.5 **Junction with U.S. 50. Continue straight ahead** into Carson City (elev. 4,675 feet). For more information on the historical beginnings of Carson City, refer to page 78.

The mountain at 3:00 is Prison Hill. The north end of the hill consists primarily of Jurassic(?) metamorphosed volcanic rock. The southern part is light-colored, knobby Cretaceous granodiorite.

28.4 The Nevada State Railroad Museum is on the left at South Carson Street (U.S. 395) and Fairview Drive. Some of the steam locomotives, coaches, and freight cars used on the V & T are on display here. The museum offers changing exhibits, train and handcar rides, lectures, and a variety of special events (refer to page 81 for a history of the V & T Railroad).

Just behind the railroad depot, the abrupt rise in the ground surface marks a normal fault. The marshy area is probably fed by springs issuing from the fault.

Eagle Valley is another structural depression along the eastern margin of the Carson Range. The easternmost fault scarps (more than one from here north to Reno) of the Sierra Nevada frontal fault zone are very close to the freeway and to homes in this small city. The risk of structural damage from an earthquake is high.

Genoa fault scarp at the base of the Carson Range in Jacks Valley just north of Genoa (photo taken just before sundown to accentuate the fault scarp, the dark line between the hills and the flat valley floor).

29.3 Nevada State Legislature building is on the right.

29.5 The State Capitol, on the right, was built in 1871 from sandstone quarried 3 miles to the east at Prison Hill. The building was completely restored in the 1980s.

29.8 The Nugget Casino on the right has one of the finest displays of native gold (crystalline and nugget) in the West, just inside the front entrance.

Just ahead on the left at Robinson Street is the Nevada State Museum. The exhibits—which include plate tectonics, minerals, archeology and anthropology, a life-sized mine, and geologic time as depicted by marine life—are very well done and stimulating for all ages. A walking tour brochure for the historical section of Carson City is available at the museum bookstore.

This building was constructed as a U.S. Mint in 1866 from the same sandstone used for the State Capitol. Nearly $50 million in gold and silver coins bearing the "CC" mint mark were minted here between 1866 and 1893.

Ahead one block on the right (Washington Street) is the former V & T Railroad depot.

30.0 Junction with U.S. 50 on the right and end of Trip C.

V & T depot in Carson City in 1872.

Nevada Historical Society photo.

TRIP D—RENO TO PYRAMID LAKE

This trip begins in Reno and follows the Truckee River to its final destination, Pyramid Lake, a remnant of Pleistocene Lake Lahontan, nested between dry desert ranges. The Truckee River has cut a majestic canyon mainly in thick flows of basalt and andesite. Lapping onto these dark igneous rocks are white layered sediments deposited by ancient Lake Lahontan—this is a great trip to study the processes of sedimentation. Almost the entire route is along highways in fault-controlled valleys, a reminder of the active tectonism responsible for today's scenery. The early immigrants used parts of this route on their way to California. The I-80 part closely follows the Truckee River portion of the California Trail, all or parts of which were used by such famous parties as Ogden in 1826, Bidwell in 1841, Frémont in 1845, and Donner in 1846. On the return to Sparks, the route passes through mining districts and rocks of explosive volcanic origin. The dry climate and sparse, but hardy, vegetation reflect the rain shadow effect of the Sierra Nevada. The trip is 100 miles long. Service stations are available near Wadsworth and just southwest of the lake on the return to Sparks. Bring drinking water with you. **Do not pull off on the soft shoulders** of the road along Pyramid Lake; use only established turnouts to avoid getting stuck in the sand.

0.0 Begin at the main entrance to the University of Nevada, Reno at Ninth and Center Streets. **Set your odometer to 0.0 and turn right onto Ninth Street.** Proceed one block.

0.1 **Turn left on Virginia Street.** Cross over the I-80 freeway.

0.2 Turn left (east) and proceed two blocks onto the I-80 East on-ramp.

0.4 Entering I-80.

This stretch of I-80 is built on late Pleistocene outwash laid down by the Truckee River (see geologic map on page 20).

The Truckee River drains the Lake Tahoe basin and other valleys north of the Lake Tahoe. It flows north out of Lake Tahoe, then turns east toward Reno and continues its eastward course until taking a final bend northward at Wadsworth to end in Pyramid Lake, a total distance of about 100 miles. The route is largely fault controlled. The Truckee River was named for Chief Truckee of the Paiute Nation.

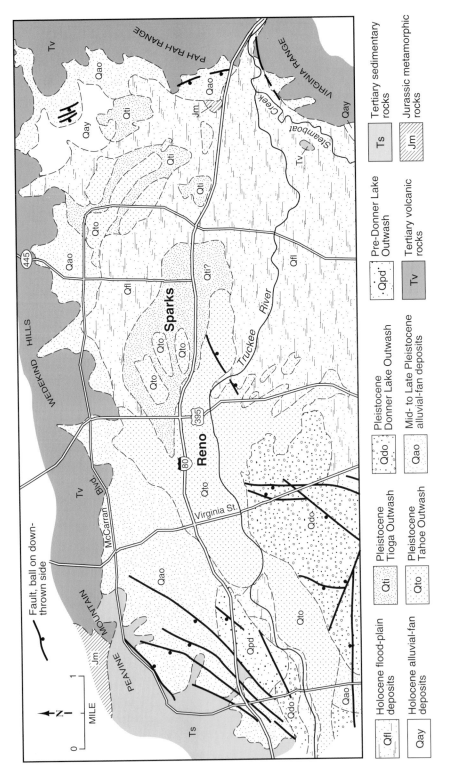

Generalized surface geology of the northern Truckee Meadows (modified after Bell and others, 1984).

Legend:

Fault, ball on down-thrown side

Qfl — Holocene flood-plain deposits

Qay — Holocene alluvial-fan deposits

Qti — Pleistocene Tioga Outwash

Qto — Pleistocene Tahoe Outwash

Qdo — Pleistocene Donner Lake Outwash

Qao — Mid- to Late Pleistocene alluvial-fan deposits

Qpd — Pre-Donner Lake Outwash

Ts — Tertiary sedimentary rocks

Tv — Tertiary volcanic rocks

Jm — Jurassic metamorphic rocks

142

STRUCTURAL GEOLOGY OF THE TRUCKEE MEADOWS

This valley is underlain by a down-dropped and down-warped structural block, which is bounded by basin-and-range faults on the east and the west sides. The east-dipping rocks of the Carson Range form the western boundary, the west-dipping rocks of the Virginia Range form the eastern boundary, and the Steamboat Hills (mostly intrusive igneous rocks) form the southern boundary. The faulting and tilting that formed this valley began at least 7 million years ago (late Miocene) and are still active.

Although faults are located along the eastern and western boundaries of the valley, the major structural break responsible for the downwarped nature of the valley is about 1 mile west of the eastern boundary of the valley. Sediments about 2,800 feet thick fill the eastern part of this basin.

Eastward tilting of this underlying structural block began about 2 million years ago. The geologic and topographic evidence for this eastward tilting includes (1) local tilted rock units that were laid down horizontally in early Pliocene time, (2) the large fan-pediment surfaces developed on the western side of the valley (note the deeply incised stream channels as erosion tries to keep up with uplift), (3) the sharp truncation of the eastern margin of the basin (Pleistocene outwash deposits from the Sierra Nevada are being buried by Holocene alluvium here), and (4) the shifting of surface drainage to the eastern margin of the valley.

3.4 Crossing over John Ascuaga's Nugget Hotel and Casino in Sparks.

Sparks was established by the Southern Pacific Railroad in 1904 to replace Wadsworth as the main switching yard and repair and crew-change facility. Note the Southern Pacific Railroad depot on the right. Fill was brought from the Helm's gravel pit (a short distance ahead) to raise the level of this former marsh 18 inches before the railroad could build its facility here.

4.1 McCarran Blvd. exit.

4.5 Rattlesnake Mountain protrudes above the southern Truckee Meadows.

4.9 At 10:00, the Helm's gravel pit is in late Pleistocene outwash, but the route from here all the way through the Truckee River canyon crosses Holocene alluvium deposited by the Truckee River.

The low marshy area north and south of I-80 is the Truckee Meadows from which the entire valley takes its name. The marshy character of this portion of the valley is due to recent uplifting of the Virginia Range (straight ahead) and eastward tilting of the valley.

Nevada Historical Society photo.

The city of Sparks and a roundhouse of the Southern Pacific Railroad in the 1920s.

These movements cause the waters from the Truckee River and its tributaries to pond here as they funnel downstream through the narrow canyon ahead. The immigrants emerging from this canyon on their westward trek to California had to skirt the marshy area by traveling south on the foothills of the Virginia Range to the north end of Rattlesnake Mountain, where they could cross the width of the valley (refer to map on page 17).

In December 1955, this section of the highway was closed due to flooding. Again, in February 1986, after several days of torrential spring rainfall, floodwaters came very near the road surface and caused extensive damage to homes in this area.

5.4 Sparks Blvd. exit. The gravel pits ahead at 11:00 are in fan deposits of at least Pleistocene age, based on the soil horizons.

6.3 Vista exit. The route is entering the Truckee River canyon which cuts through the Virginia Range on the right and the Pah Rah Range on the left ("Pa-rah" is the Paiute word for "river").

6.7 Jurassic(?) metamorphosed volcanic and volcaniclastic sedimentary rocks are exposed in the roadcut on the left, and on both sides of the road for the next 2 to 3 miles.

To the right and farther downstream, small rapids mark the areas where the Army Corps of Engineers removed "reefs" of Mesozoic rocks (that partially blocked the river channel) to reduce the effects of flooding in the eastern portion of the Truckee Meadows.

The Truckee River follows the Olinghouse fault zone (a probable strike-slip fault zone with left-lateral offset) from Sparks to Wadsworth, where it joins the Walker Lane fault zone (refer to maps on pages 80 and 81). Based on newspaper and verbal accounts, a major earthquake occurred on the east-west Olinghouse fault in 1869 rupturing the surface, probably near the Olinghouse mining district north of Wadsworth. See photo on page 163.

The river probably existed in middle to late Tertiary time before warping and faulting uplifted the Virginia Range beginning in the Miocene, but was able to downcut its valley at about the same rate that the range was being uplifted, therefore maintaining its course. Uplift continues today.

The Pah Rah Range will be on the left (north) as you travel to Wadsworth. It is an L-shaped range bounded on the south by the Olinghouse fault zone and on the east by the Walker Lane fault zone. The range is composed of Oligocene through Pliocene andesite basalt, tuff, breccia, conglomerate, mudflows, and a few rhyolite plugs, domes and flows, all of which overlie a basement of metamorphic and granitic rocks.

On the right (south) is the Virginia Range. The rocks along this route are mainly early Miocene andesite flows, overlain (farther ahead) by Miocene rhyolite and andesite flows, tuff, and mudflow breccia. Local deposits of diatomite, tuff, shale, and sandstone are also found in the range.

7.6 A regional northeast-trending fault crosses the river here. On the left, flows, lahars, tuffs, and related sedimentary rocks (on the west) are in fault contact with metamorphosed igneous rocks.

8.4 More reefs were removed from the Truckee River channel in the next 1 to 1.5 miles. Rapids mark the end of the channel deepening.

9.3 Lockwood exit. Lagomarsino Canyon is at 2:00. Houses are built on the Truckee River floodplain.

The youngest volcanic rock recognized in this area is a thin Pleistocene basalt exposed high on the west side of Lagomarsino Canyon. It flowed from McClelland Peak 9 miles to the southeast down the ancestral Lagomarsino Canyon about 1 million years ago. Since that time, Lagomarsino Canyon has deepened more than 150 feet, and the Truckee River has deepened 70 feet at the mouth of the canyon.

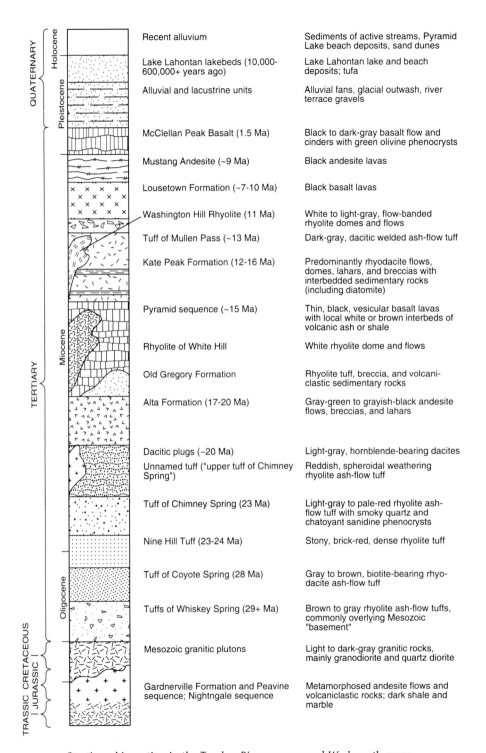

QUATERNARY	Holocene	Recent alluvium	Sediments of active streams, Pyramid Lake beach deposits, sand dunes
		Lake Lahontan lakebeds (10,000-600,000+ years ago)	Lake Lahontan lake and beach deposits; tufa
	Pleistocene	Alluvial and lacustrine units	Alluvial fans, glacial outwash, river terrace gravels
		McClellan Peak Basalt (1.5 Ma)	Black to dark-gray basalt flow and cinders with green olivine phenocrysts
TERTIARY	Miocene	Mustang Andesite (~9 Ma)	Black andesite lavas
		Lousetown Formation (~7-10 Ma)	Black basalt lavas
		Washington Hill Rhyolite (11 Ma)	White to light-gray, flow-banded rhyolite domes and flows
		Tuff of Mullen Pass (~13 Ma)	Dark-gray, dacitic welded ash-flow tuff
		Kate Peak Formation (12-16 Ma)	Predominantly rhyodacite flows, domes, lahars, and breccias with interbedded sedimentary rocks (including diatomite)
		Pyramid sequence (~15 Ma)	Thin, black, vesicular basalt lavas with local white or brown interbeds of volcanic ash or shale
		Rhyolite of White Hill	White rhyolite dome and flows
		Old Gregory Formation	Rhyolite tuff, breccia, and volcaniclastic sedimentary rocks
		Alta Formation (17-20 Ma)	Gray-green to grayish-black andesite flows, breccias, and lahars
		Dacitic plugs (~20 Ma)	Light-gray, hornblende-bearing dacites
		Unnamed tuff ("upper tuff of Chimney Spring")	Reddish, spheroidal weathering rhyolite ash-flow tuff
		Tuff of Chimney Spring (23 Ma)	Light-gray to pale-red rhyolite ash-flow tuff with smoky quartz and chatoyant sanidine phenocrysts
	Oligocene	Nine Hill Tuff (23-24 Ma)	Stony, brick-red, dense rhyolite tuff
		Tuff of Coyote Spring (28 Ma)	Gray to brown, biotite-bearing rhyodacite ash-flow tuff
		Tuffs of Whiskey Spring (29+ Ma)	Brown to gray rhyolite ash-flow tuffs, commonly overlying Mesozoic "basement"
CRETACEOUS / JURASSIC / TRIASSIC		Mesozoic granitic plutons	Light to dark-gray granitic rocks, mainly granodiorite and quartz diorite
		Gardnerville Formation and Peavine sequence; Nightngale sequence	Metamorphosed andesite flows and volcaniclastic rocks; dark shale and marble

Stratigraphic section in the Truckee River canyon and Wadsworth areas.

146

Lagomarsino Canyon (on the far left) looking southeast from the Truckee River. A basalt flow forms a thin mantle on the cliffs to the right of the canyon in the middle of the photo.

A rhyolite dome rises in the background. In the foreground (above and below I-80) contorted volcanic rocks are exposed in the roadcuts.

147

All-Lite lightweight aggregate facility near Lockwood.

Pleistocene basalt forming a low hill just south of Mustang.

The scabland-like erosion of the Pleistocene basalt and the presence of granitic boulders derived from the Carson Range at least 15 miles to the west indicate that catastrophic floods issued periodically down the Truckee River during Pleistocene glacial times.

High on the right, up Lagomarsino Canyon, 11-million-year-old rhyolite is mined for lightweight aggregate.

9.9 Look up the drainageway at 9:00 on the skyline to see a dome of light-colored rhyolite dated at about 8 million years old.

10.6 A thin cap of basalt crops out on the low hill just to the left of I-80. The basalt flowed across and probably dammed the Truckee River about 1.5 million years ago.

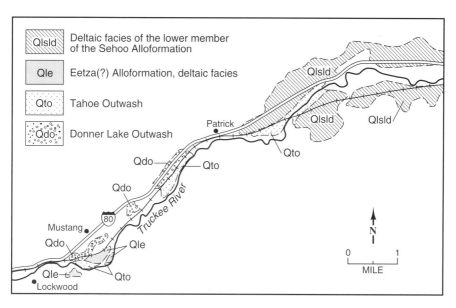

Pleistocene Lake Lahontan and glacial outwash deposits in the Truckee River canyon near Mustang (Trexler and Pease, 1981; Bell and others, 1984).

The first delta deposits of the Truckee River (where it emptied into Pleistocene Lake Lahontan) are exposed between the current river channel and I-80 here.

10.7 Mustang exit. Miocene andesite is exposed to the right, across the river, where it lies on eroded flows and sedimentary rocks.

On the right, the terrace surface nearest I-80 is composed of older Pleistocene glacial outwash. Toward the river, a lower terrace is composed of younger glacial outwash.

149

12.3 At this point the Truckee River canyon opens up to exhibit vast expanses of Tertiary volcanic rocks. Contorted white tuffs are just ahead on both sides of the canyon.

14.5 Faulted and contorted tuffs in the roadcut on the left.

14.6 **Scenic view stop ahead. Turn off to the right.** (Color photo on page 39.)

The highway, railroad, electric transmission lines, and natural gas and petroleum pipelines use this river route through the mountains, as did the immigrants to California beginning with the Stephens-Murphy-Townsend party in 1844. These early travelers had to make some 40 river crossings to negotiate the canyon's difficult terrain. The opening of the Central Pacific Railroad in 1868-69 brought the wagon train period to a close. In 1917, the road through the canyon became a portion of State Road 1, which in 1920 became the Nevada section of the Victory Highway. When federal highway names were replaced by a numerical system in 1925, the Victory Highway became U.S. 40. In 1958, after reconstruction, this route became the initial section of I-80 in Nevada.

The small houses at the bottom of the hill sit near a high water mark of ancient Lake Lahontan at an elevation of 4,313 feet. Truckee River delta and Lahontan lake deposits have been found at elevations as high as 4,380 feet in this part of the canyon.

This is near the western limit of ancient Lake Lahontan in the Truckee River canyon. From here eastward, the Truckee River formed a series of deltas in the lake.

LAKE LAHONTAN

Lake Lahontan, named by Clarence King during his 1870s Exploration of the Fortieth Parallel in honor of the French officer and traveler, Baron de Lahontan, was a large lake that existed mainly in western Nevada and eastern California during the last two thirds of the Pleistocene Epoch. Locally, glaciers in the Sierra Nevada increased and decreased in extent with changes in the climate throughout the Pleistocene. The climate was wetter and cooler during glacial periods, which contributed to the increased amount of surface water in this area.

At its maximum during the most recent glacial period, Lake Lahontan was the second largest pluvial lake in the Western Hemisphere (Lake Bonneville in Utah was the largest). It covered an area of almost 8,500 square miles (about the size of Lake Erie), and reached a maximum depth of about 920 feet at what is now Pyramid Lake, 525 feet at Walker Lake, and 490 feet at the Carson Sink, all present-day remnants of the ancient lake, fed by rivers flowing from the Sierra Nevada.

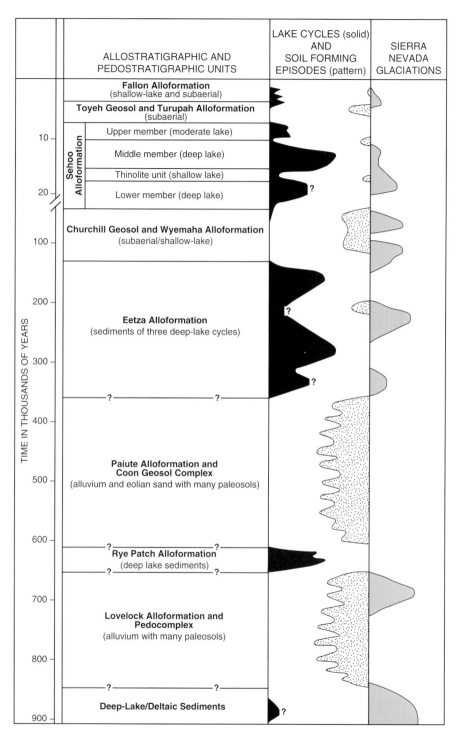

Lake Lahontan cycles, related stratigraphic units, and Sierra Nevada glaciations (after Birkeland, 1964, 1968; Fullerton, 1986; Morrison, 1991).

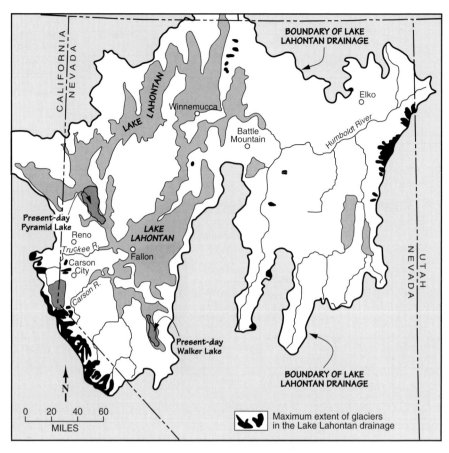

Maximum extent of Lake Lahontan (after Morrison, 1964).

In the last 75,000 years there have been four measurable high lake stands that correlate to Sierran glacial advances, wetter climate, and thicker lake-bottom deposits. The last maximum lake stand was about 13,000 years ago.

Today, the ancient strandlines rim the mountains slopes surrounding the lake's former basins. They are prominently displayed around Pyramid Lake. The longer the lake remained at a particular level, the more prominent the strandline or wave-cut terrace became. Some local terraces are as much as 300 feet wide. Only one terrace is actually cut into rock. The lake level usually fluctuated too rapidly to accomplish more than just notching the pre-existing alluvium.

15.2 Passing the Patrick exit, named in honor of Patrick McCarran, a powerful and influential U.S. Senator from 1932 to 1954. Ahead on the right, Lake Lahontan deltaic sands and gravels are being mined for aggregate material.

15.8 Lake Lahontan sediments are seen in roadcuts on the left. These horizontal and varved sediments are exposed in the canyon from here on. The dark rocks resting on the sediments are derived from Miocene basalt.

17.1 On the right is Sierra Pacific Power Company's Tracy Power Station which opened in the fall of 1963. It consists of three units of 53, 83, and 110 megawatt capacity. This steam generating plant is designed to run on either natural gas or fuel oil. A new generating plant (under construction in 1995) will provide power from natural gas turbine generators.

17.6 More good exposures of Lahontan lake sediments are on the left.

18.6 More sand and gravel operations on the right.

18.7 Tracy-Clark Station exit.

Just beyond the Clark exit are thick exposures of laminated lake sediments that were deposited in the delta of the Truckee River where

Horizontal Lake Lahontan sediments along I-80.

it fed into ancient Lake Lahontan during maximum lake level. Gianella (1933) noted that the Lake Lahontan sediments were laid down as isolated patches in quiet water along the walls of the Truckee River canyon, instead of completely filling the canyon, as might be expected.

19.9 The Eagle-Picher Minerals, Inc. Clark plant on the right produces diatomite for use as absorbants, abrasives, filter material, insulation, and filler in many consumer products.

The diatomite is being mined from a lacustrine unit within a section of Miocene rhyolite flows at the Celatom quarry located about 7 miles to the east. Diatomite is composed of the white, siliceous skeletal remains of diatoms, which are microscopic, single-celled plants (algae) that still grow today in fresh and marine water. The predominate diatom found in these beds is *Melosira granulata*. Diatoms absorb silica from water and biologically secrete it to form their siliceous shells in a great variety of forms. Enormous numbers of shells accumulate to form deposits of diatomaceous earth or diatomite. Almost all of the uses of diatomite are based upon its unique natural microscopic structure.

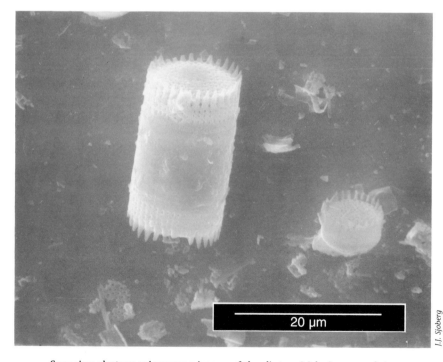

20 µm

J.J. Sjoberg

Scanning electron microscope image of the diatom Melosira granulata.

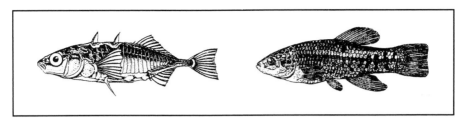

Fossil fish—Nevada stickleback (left) and Nevada Killifish (right)—found in abandoned diatomite quarries east of Fernley, Nevada (Courtesy of Tom Lugaski).

Many sedimentary rocks contain diatoms; however, the term "diatomite" is reserved for those deposits of pure opaline or hydrous silica that have a quality and purity necessary for commercial uses. The diatomite deposits we see in this area were formed in bodies of freshwater during late Miocene. Associated with these diatomite deposits are fossil fish and leaves. Abandoned quarries east of Fernley are good places to find these fossils. Remember, always obey "no trespassing" signs.

There are hundreds of industrial uses for diatomite including filtration (of water, beer, and sugar syrup), as a mineral filler or extender (in paper, plastics, paints, insecticides, and matches), as high-temperature insulation, as an absorbent (for oils), as a mild abrasive (in polishes), in process applications such as brick, admixture or pozzolan for cement, and as a conditioning agent to prevent caking.

22.2 Ahead, on the left, an artificial oxbow lake was created when the Truckee River was diverted to the south during construction of the freeway.

On the left near road level is a thick sequence of basalt flows with some interbedded rhyolitic tuff, clastic and tuffaceous sedimentary rocks, and occasional lenses of diatomite. Overlying these rocks are andesite flows.

22.7 Derby Dam is at 3:00 at the base of the hills. Note the thick stands of "rushes," called phragmites. It is one of the larger stands still used by local American Indians. In prehistoric and historic times, these people gathered a sweet substance (actually produced by aphids) from the plants. The long straight shafts of phragmites were used for composite arrow shafts, and sometimes woven together with slender rushes to make mats and fishing weirs.

American Indians in the Great Basin had a practical use for nearly everything that swam, flew, grew, or ranged over their territory. Plants such as willows, cattails, reeds, and rushes were woven into baskets, trays, cradles, mats, boats, sandals, and clothing.

155

Phragmites were used by the Paiutes for food and arrow shafts.

Juniper and cottonwood were used for bows, walking staffs, pinyon hooks, and digging sticks. The people who lived in this area around 2,000 years ago made duck decoys from tules (reeds) covered with duck skins.

23.7   Thisbe-Derby Dam exit. Miocene volcanic rocks are on the left and the right. This small concrete and earthen dam diverts water from the Truckee River via the Truckee-Carson Canal southeastward to the Lahontan Reservoir on the Carson River. Construction began on Derby and Lahontan Dams and the connecting diversion channels in 1903 as part of the Newlands Reclamation Project (named after Francis G. Newlands, Nevada Congressman who sponsored the reclamation bill). It was the first U.S. Government project authorized under the Reclamation Act of 1902. The first water was diverted through the canal in 1906. In years of normal or above normal precipitation, this project can provide year-round irrigation to over 90,000 acres, mainly in the Fallon area about 30 miles to the east.

This and other historic dams along the Truckee were responsible for the eventual extinction in the 1940s of the "salmon" trout, one of the historic staple foods of the Pyramid Lake Paiutes, because they prevented the fish from making their upstream spawning runs. Derby Dam did not include a fish ladder for upstream spawning runs. The fish would mill below the dam by the thousands only to be trapped, netted, dynamited, or hooked. Newspaper stories printed at the time said that a person could walk across the river below the dam and not get his feet wet. The diversion of the Truckee River's water continued to lower the lake level and so clog the delta with sediment that the trout that didn't get caught at the dam couldn't return to the lake after spawning. Restocking of the lake's fish population with related subspecies from other lakes began in the 1950s.

24.8 High in the dark-colored hills at 2:00 are the white waste dumps of Eagle-Picher's Celatom mine which supplies diatomite to their processing plant at Clark Station. The white band in the lower canyon wall is volcanic tuff, not diatomite. Diatomite can be easily confused with pure volcanic ash deposits in this area until you view the distinctly different textures of the two under a hand lens.

25.8 Orchard Exit.

27.0 Painted Rock exit. The gray and tan rocks on the left are andesite flows and clastic rocks. Farther along, the pink and white rocks are volcanic

Eagle-Picher Minerals, Inc. Celatom mine.

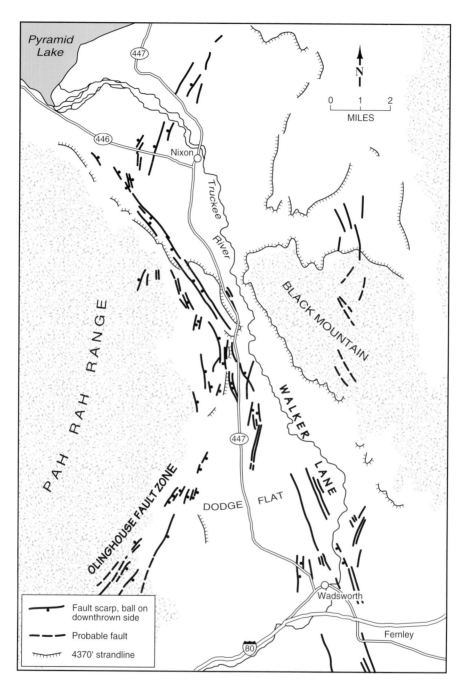

Late Quaternary faults and the Lahontan 4,370-foot strandline in the Walker Lane and Olinghouse fault zones area just south of Pyramid Lake (Bell, 1984).

158

ash-flow tuffs (22 to 28 million years old) that have been partly altered to clay minerals by hydrothermal fluids (refer to page 43 for a detailed explanation of this process). These brightly colored rocks unconformably overlie Mesozoic granite and metamorphosed sedimentary rocks. The hills beyond these roadcuts on the left are composed of Miocene basalt. The volcanic rocks are tilted to the west and horizontal, beige, much younger Lake Lahontan sediments lie uncomfortably on them, filling the gullies.

27.4 Ahead on the left, Lake Lahontan sediments lie on Oligocene and early Miocene rhyolitic ash-flow tuffs.

The Lahontan Beach (the beach deposit of the highest lake level, 4,370 feet) is visible as a strandline terrace on a rocky hill ahead on the south (right) side of the Truckee River.

27.8 Ahead on both sides of the road are more Lake Lahontan sediments, and on the right are Miocene volcanic rocks.

30.0 A conical knob of Miocene basalt rises above the hills on the left. More Lake Lahontan sediments and terraces can be seen to the left.

30.3 On the hillside at 10:00 are the concrete remains of a 50-stamp mill for the Olinghouse (White Horse) gold mining district located 6 miles to the northwest. The Olinghouse area was first prospected in 1860. In 1906, The Nevada Consolidated Mining Company built a railroad linking the mines at Olinghouse to this mill. The mill operated for only 3 months in 1906 and 1907, due to insufficient ore supplies.

30.6 **Turn right onto the Wadsworth-Pyramid Lake exit. At the stop sign turn left to access State Route 447.**

31.2 **Entering the Pyramid Lake Indian Reservation. You must purchase a day permit if you stop anywhere on the reservation.** These may be purchased at the Smokeshop here, at the Marina in Sutcliffe, at the fishing store on the Pyramid Lake Highway (State Route 446) just west of the lake, or at the Tribal Offices in Nixon. You can be cited and fined if you are caught stopping without a permit.

This is the approximate intersection of the east-northeast-trending Olinghouse fault zone and the northwest-trending Walker Lane fault zone (refer to maps on pages 80 and 81).

32.4 Just before entering Wadsworth, **turn left on State Route 447 to Nixon and Pyramid Lake.**

WADSWORTH

Wadsworth was the site of a seasonal Paiute village when John C. Frémont camped there on January 6, 1844, after passing by Pyramid Lake. In the late 1840s Wadsworth, then known as Lower Emigrant Crossing and Drytown, became a watering stop for those emigrants who survived the terrible "Forty Mile Desert" (Carson Sink) and were continuing on to California via the Truckee River (refer to map on page 17 for early immigrant trails through the Truckee Meadows). Seasonal trading posts were common here beginning with one built by William Gregory in 1854. In the early 1860s, immigrants began to settle here, and in 1868 the Central Pacific Railroad reached Wadsworth from California, set up its supply and maintenance headquarters, and laid out a town named in honor of Civil War officer James S. Wadsworth. It became a prominent railroad town and supply junction for freight wagons serving mining camps to the south.

Nevada Historical Society photo.

Wadsworth in 1903.

NAMING OF THE TRUCKEE RIVER

The Truckee River was named at Wadsworth on October 9, 1844 by the Elisha Stevens emigrant party. The party was camped at the Humboldt Sink to the northeast after having finished a grueling crossing of the Forty Mile Desert and was debating whether to finish their trek to California when a

Paiute chief befriended them. As he dropped his robe to show that he came in peace and was unarmed, the chief repeated a word that sounded like "tro-kay" to the white men, which was the Paiute word for "all right" or "very well." He told them of a river just a few days away that would lead them straight to the Sierra Nevada. He led the party to the present site of Wadsworth and the river, the first fresh water they had had in a long time. They were so grateful that they named the river "Truckee's River." Earlier that same year John C. Frémont had met the Paiute chief at Pyramid Lake and had named the river the "Salmon-Trout River." The name never caught on, and Frémont renamed the river after his friend and guide, "Captain Truckee."

32.9 The road ascends a large fault-scarp hill. Three north-trending faults cross the road here, a part of the Walker Lane fault zone.

This area is part of the Carson Desert and is one of the driest and warmest parts of northern Nevada because of its moderate elevation and position in the rain shadow of the Sierra Nevada. The climate is extreme continental, with warm summers (highs are usually in the low 90s), cold winters (the temperature may dip below -5 °F), and a wide diurnal temperature range. Annual precipitation averages less than 5 inches. The precipitation can vary widely from year to year in this desert area—extremes in annual recorded rainfall range from 2 to 8 inches. Periods of above or below normal precipitation can last from 2 to 20 years. Wind is common here. Sudden brief, but strong, windstorms occur in the spring and fall and redistribute much dust and sand.

Vegetation consists mainly of desert shrubs, herbs, and grasses. It is closely controlled by soil conditions and drainage. Greasewood, shadscale, and sagebrush dominate the low mountains and well-drained lowland areas. Mormon tea occurs locally throughout the area, and hopsage and white sage occur in the transition zone between the mountains and lowlands. Other plant associations are restricted to relatively small areas of abnormal soil, drainage conditions, or eolian sand. Greasewood is found in saline clayey soil at the margins of playas and poorly drained lowlands where the subsoil is always moist, but the surface dries to a crust in late summer. Two species of rabbitbrush grow where the ground has been disturbed. Desert saltgrass is found in areas that

Greasewood

Shadscale

161

Vegetation characteristic of the Carson Desert: hopsage on the left, rabbitbrush, sagebrush, and grasses.

border the more permanent playas, ponds, streams, and marshes, where soils are moderately to strongly saline. Cottonwood and willow (the only native trees in the area) and big sagebrush border stream courses and some lakes where the soil is not saline. Russian olive, an exotic tree, is also widespread among the cottonwoods and willows. Scattered junipers grow in the higher elevations.

Animal life includes the collared, horned, whip-tailed, swift, and leopard lizards; the poisonous Great Basin rattlesnake; muledeer; coyotes; rabbits; bobcats; antelope ground squirrels; kangaroo rats; and tarantulas. The great herds of mountain sheep present when Frémont passed through here are gone.

34.7 The road on the left leads to the Olinghouse mining district. Note the colorful hills ahead and on the left—another example of hydrothermal alteration in Oligocene-early Miocene rhyolitic ash-flow tuffs.

The Olinghouse mining district was first prospected in 1860. The gold orebodies in the district occur as small, high-grade pockets in quartz and calcite veins emplaced along fault zones associated with Miocene dacite dikes that intrude Tertiary basalt and interbedded sedimentary rocks. Native gold, pyrite, sparse chalcopyrite, and bornite occur in veinlets in the dikes. Mineralization occurred about 10.5

SOUTHERN PAH RAH RANGE

Olinghouse fault scarp

John Bell photo.

Aerial photo of the Olinghouse fault, looking northwest.

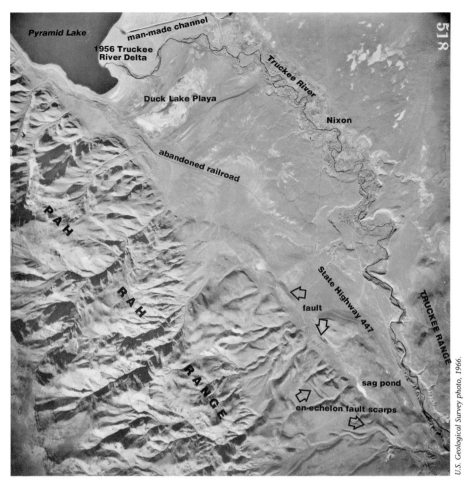

Aerial photo of the Truckee River and Route 447 in the Walker Lane between Wadsworth on the south and Pyramid Lake on the north. The major northwest-trending fault zone of the Walker Lane cuts Pleistocene gravels south and east of Pyramid Lake. Sag ponds (white areas) are developed along the main rift. Note the swarm of en-echelon fault scarps on the southwest side of the main rift.

million years ago. Underground and placer mining methods were used here.

35.5 Entering Dodge Flat. The area on both sides of the road consists of a thin veneer of reworked sand deposits that overlie lake sediments of Lake Lahontan. It is characterized by the widespread occurrence of dendritic tufa.

The eastern portion of Dodge Flat (and extending northward to Pyramid Lake) is transected by segments of the Walker Lane right-lateral, strike-slip fault zone. Geomorphic features marking this zone are rift valleys, long linear ridges, subtle scarps, sag ponds, and vegetation alignments.

Note the horizontal benches of Lake Lahontan strandlines near the base of the Truckee Range to the right. The Truckee Range is composed of basalt that flowed from two or three large shield volcanoes 9 to 10 million years ago.

On the left, the southern end of the Pah Rah Range consists of basalt flows which overlie Oligocene and early Miocene silicic ash-flow tuffs and underlie rhyodacite flows and domes.

38.4 Leaving Dodge Flat

39.3 At 10:00 on the horizon behind the telephone poles, some subtle faults can be seen. Northwest-trending faults have offset (sliced through) Pleistocene alluvial fan deposits, which normally form

Steep-faced fault scarps dissect alluvial fan deposits on the east side of the Pah Rah Range (middle of photo). Below the fault scarps are low, continuous strandlines of the former Lake Lahonton.

String of cui-ui.

Nevada Historical Society photo.

smooth surfaces but now descend step-like from the base of the Pah
Rah Range. Most offsets are less than 10 feet.

40.3 Turn right to Numana Hatchery Visitors Center.

41.0 Stop to visit the hatchery and small museum. There is a larger
museum at the Marina at Sutcliffe. The hatchery has been working to
protect and preserve the cui-ui, a fish protected under the
Endangered Species Act.

Pyramid Lake is brackish and contains about 5,000 parts per million of dissolved salts, about 75 percent of which is sodium chloride.
The pH of the lake is 9.15; the range is 6.5 to 8.5 in most lakes. These
conditions are well-tolerated by the present fish population of the cui-
ui, cutthroat trout, and the Sacramento perch. The cui-ui, a black
sucker fish, is found only in Pyramid Lake, although fossils of its
Pleistocene ancestors are found in the sediments of Klamath and
Utah Lakes. Cui-ui was a food staple of the Pyramid Lake Paiutes and
the namesake of the Paiute tribe's ancestors, the "Kuyuidokado,"
which means "cui-ui eaters."

Fishermen today regularly catch 5- to 16-pound trout from
Pyramid Lake. The best fishing is from October to May when the water
is cool enough for the trout to move closer to the surface. The fishing
success in recent years can be attributed to an extensive fishery

restoration program undertaken by the Pyramid Lake Tribe in the 1970s. One of the complex problems encountered in this program was raising cold-water fish in the middle of the desert where fresh water is at a premium. The hatcheries recycle 95 percent of all the fresh water used. Since the facilities became operational in 1974, about 2.8 million cutthroat and between 10 and 18 million cui-ui are stocked each year.

Retrace route to main road.

41.8 At the main road, turn right to continue on the route.

The white deposits across the river are sediments of Lake Lahontan. The light-colored horizontal lines above these deposits mark high stands of Lake Lahontan (see color photo on page 39). The highest measured strandline of Lake Lahontan in this area is at an elevation of 4,370 feet. The sedimentary record of Lake Lahontan exposed in the cliffs to the east reflects periods of deep and shallow water, periods when sediment was being deposited and periods when sediment was being eroded, the changing position of the river channel and its deltas through Pleistocene time, wave direction, and tectonism, among other things. Geologists study such details as the size and composition of the sediment grains and the changes in

Photo looking northeast across the Truckee River at a thick section of Lake Lahontan sediments.

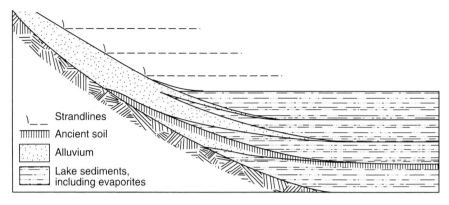

Strandlines
Ancient soil
Alluvium
Lake sediments,
including evaporites

Schematic section of part of a pluvial lake basin (now dry), showing common relations among alluvium, lake sediments, ancient soils, and strandlines. Three pluvial lake phases are indicated (Flint, 1967).

them over time (the thickness of the individual soil units, the presence of oxidation in the soil layers) to be able to recreate a picture of the dynamic interaction of Sierran glaciers, the Truckee River, and Lake Lahontan during the Pleistocene.

Along the perimeter of the highest strandline are stone hunting blinds built around pits by the nomadic ancestors of the present-day Paiutes. These ancient people lived in caves and sites along the shores perhaps as long ago as 11,000 years.

42.5 Roadcuts are in alluvium shed from the Pah Rah Range to the west.

43.4 Turn off to the right at the historical marker.

PYRAMID LAKE INDIAN WAR

Until the spring of 1860, the Paiutes (with a population of 5,000 to 7,000 at that time) remained friendly with the white settlers and prospectors crossing their land, but friction began to increase between the two groups as settlers began flocking to the Comstock Lode.

In May 1860, the Paiutes, Bannocks, and Shoshones gathered at Pyramid Lake to discuss the problems related to the growing flood of non-Indians. All of the leaders, except for Numaga (Young Winnemucca), were in favor of war. Numaga might have won the rest of the council over to his views if the Williams' Station incident hadn't just occurred.

Williams' Station was located on the Carson River about 2 miles east of present-day Silver Springs. Several men, who had been left in charge of the station in Williams' absence, had abducted and raped two Paiute women from the Walker Lake area who were married to men from the Bannock tribe. Paiute and Shoshone men visiting the station discovered the missing women and rushed back to inform the chief of the Bannocks. The chief dispatched a band of warriors to avenge the women. Four white men were killed and the station was burned to the ground.

News of the situation at Williams' Station reached Virginia City on May 7th. Panicked and outraged, a volunteer "army" was hastily assembled from the Virginia City-Genoa region and, under the command of Major Ormsby, rode north to do battle with the Paiutes.

Nevada Historical Society photo.

Near this site on May 12th, the Paiutes confronted the whites and forced them to retreat towards Wadsworth. The Paiutes counted 46 dead whites, but 70 white volunteers were never accounted for. On June 2, the army returned with 65 volunteers and 207 regular U.S. Army troops under the command of Col. John Hays. A battle was fought in the meadows south of Pyramid Lake and northward into the steep mountain terrain of the Lake Range. The Paiute warriors held off the white army until the main body of women, children, and older men escaped to the north. Because they carried their dead with them as they retreated, the Paiute casualties remain unknown. Because of this sequence of incidents, Fort Churchill was constructed on the Carson River later in 1860 and a peace treaty was negotiated.

Photo of Numaga (Young Winnemucca) the great Paiute leader during the Pyramid Lake Wars.

TUFA

On the ledges behind and below the historical marker are good exposures of lithoid or stony tufa. Light gray tufa is conspicuous at desert lakes such as Pyramid Lake, Walker Lake, and the Great Salt Lake, and at the Red Sea. Limy minerals, aided by the activity of the cyanobacteria (blue-green algae) that thrive in these lakes, precipitate out of the brackish,

Lithoid tufa (near the Pyramid Lake Indian Wars Historical Marker).

mineral-laden water to form tufa underwater and on shoreline rocks and beaches.

In 1885, Russell classified the tufa deposits of Lake Lahontan into three varieties: (1) **lithoid** (stony, compact), (2) **dendritic** (coralline, branching; see photos on pages 173 and 178), and (3) **thinolite** (spheroidal, concentric bands of thinolite crystals; see photos on page 178). There are many hot springs in and around these lakes that aid in the deposition of thinolite tufa from the mineral-rich waters.

44.6 Turn off to the right at the top of the hill.

The route has ascended a Lake Lahontan terrace. On the right side of the road are good examples of well-developed tufa heads. These tufas have both lithoid and dendritic forms. Exposure to the atmosphere and greater salinity during lower lake levels are believed to have promoted rapid tufa growth here and in other areas of Lake Lahontan.

45.8 Note the horizontal terraces etched into Lake Lahontan sediments on the left side of the road. These mark strandlines of Lake Lahontan.

Pyramid Lake ahead. The town of Nixon lies in the patch of green at 2:00. Behind Nixon, in the middle distance at 1:00 is Marble Bluff.

170

Behind Marble Bluff is the higher Lake Range. Anaho Island is directly ahead. The Pyramid is to the right of Anaho near the eastern shore of the lake. The Truckee River runs north through Nixon and bends to the left before entering the lake at its present delta.

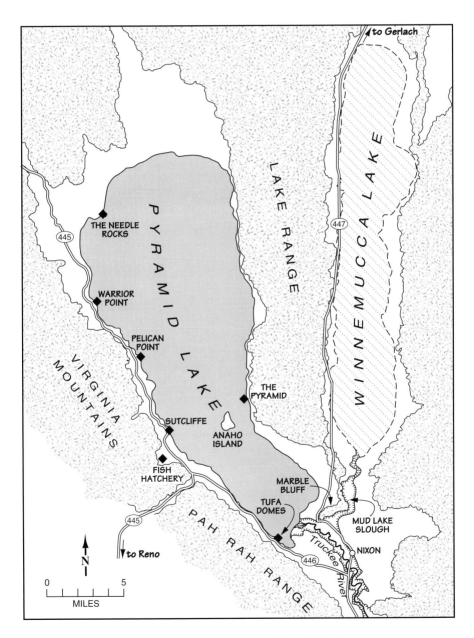

Key points of interest around Pyramid Lake.

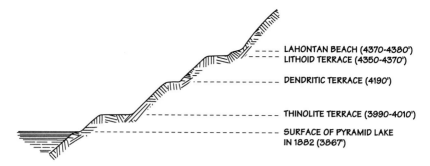

LAHONTAN BEACH (4370-4380')
LITHOID TERRACE (4350-4370')

DENDRITIC TERRACE (4190')

THINOLITE TERRACE (3990-4010')

SURFACE OF PYRAMID LAKE
IN 1882 (3867')

Generalized profile of Lake Lahontan terraces with corresponding tufa types
(after Russell, 1885).

47.3 Crossing old railroad bed of the Fernley & Lassen Railway, constructed in 1912-14.

48.9 Junction of State Routes 446 and 447. Turn left on State Route 446 to Sutcliffe (go to page 175, mile 0.0),

or

Continue straight ahead on State Route 447 to Nixon for an optional side trip to Winnemucca Lake (do not reset odometer).

OPTIONAL SIDE TRIP TO MARBLE BLUFF AND WINNEMUCCA (DRY) LAKE:

49.5 Crossing the Truckee River. The Nixon Post Office and Pyramid Lake Paiute Tribal Offices are ahead on the right. Nixon was named for George S. Nixon, U.S. Senator from Nevada (1905-1912), who sponsored development of this reservation. The site where Nixon stands was probably the location of the Paiute village documented by Fremont in 1844. The reservation's headquarters and school were built here in the 1870s.

51.4 Marble Bluff is directly ahead. It is composed of Mesozoic metamorphosed limestone and dolomite coated with massive tufa deposits.

53.0 The road to Marble Bluff Dam and the fishway are on the left.
    The drainageway along the south and east sides of the bluff is the Mud Lake Slough, the natural overflow channel from Pyramid to Winnemucca Lake. Until 1939, the Winnemucca basin contained

Dendritic tufa draping the north side of Marble Bluff.

water year-round. At its maximum historic level the lake had an area of about 90 square miles and maximum depth of about 80 feet. After 1911, inflow into Winnemucca Lake was intermittent. Because of upstream water diversions, the Truckee River downcut its present channel too deeply for water to flow eastward into Mud Lake Slough and on to Winnemucca Lake. By 1939, Winnemucca Lake was no longer perennial. A valuable fish and waterfowl habitat had been lost.

54.0 The massive tufa deposits draping the surface of the bluffs on the right are excellent examples of the Sehoo or "dendritic (tufa) terrace" stage of Lake Lahontan. Beginning about 9,000 years ago aboriginal people used the large "bubbles" in the tufa for shelter. Shelter sites and petroglyphs etched in the tufa can be found at this elevation (4,000-4,100 feet) in the valleys once filled by Lake Lahontan.

55.3 The route enters an area of windblown sand. The source of the sand is sediment from the Pyramid Lake basin. The grains are funneled through this pass by prevailing west winds.

57.3 The road crosses the pass into the Winnemucca Lake (dry) basin. "Winnemucca" is a fairly commonplace name in Nevada; it is generally agreed that the name commemorates Poito ("hole through nose," or Old Winnemucca) who was one of three famous Paiute men named Winnemucca in Nevada history. The word has a variety of interpretations, including "place by the river," "bread giver," "the giver," "the charitable man," and "one moccasin."

    Note the thick stands of Indian ricegrass thriving on these sandy soils (see color photos on page 40.) The tiny black seeds were harvested by most Great Basin Indian groups as a staple food.

57.5 Note the mounds of brown tufa on the right. These formed along the shore of Winnemucca Lake.

57.8 **Turn around on the road to the left and proceed back toward the junction of State Routes 446 and 447.**

69.1 Slow down and turn off to the right before the guard rail. On the right is the southern end of Pyramid Lake and the terminus of the Truckee River. In the foreground the Truckee has cut through ancient Lake Lahontan and more recent sediments in its terminal floodplain, due to lowering of the lake level. A manmade channel was dug in the 1930s in a futile attempt to bypass the shallow natural delta channel and facilitate upstream spawning runs of Pyramid Lake fish. Again, in the mid-1970s a smaller channel was dug within the 1930s channel for the endangered cui-ui and cutthroat. These manmade measures have proven largely unsuccessful because of the continued lowering of the lake level.

66.3 Junction of State Routes 446 and 447.

0.0 **Reset odometer to 0.0 and turn right onto State Route 446 and proceed toward Sutcliffe.**

The low terraces in this area are complex delta deposits. The northern end of the Pah Rah Range is on the left. Most of the exposed rocks in the range here are late Oligocene to early Miocene rhyolitic ash-flow tuffs. Basalt flows cap the mountain range.

1.9 Note the high strandlines of Lake Lahontan at 10:00.

2.4 Look ahead and downhill to the light-colored sandy depression traversed by State Route 446. This is Duck Lake playa (elev. 3,861 feet), the result of a Pyramid Lake shoreline barrier bar that dammed local drainage toward the north, producing a small lake fed by local runoff and probably by some groundwater seepage from Pyramid Lake during high water levels. Historically, Duck Lake was a marshy area which provided waterfowl resources for the local Paiutes. This elevation is near the historic high level of Pyramid Lake.

3.3 Crossing Duck Lake playa

The level of Pyramid Lake has fluctuated substantially during historic times because of natural climatic change and man's intervention. Frémont found the level at about 3,860 feet in 1844. The lake level began a steady decline when major water diversions began for the Newlands Irrigation Project at Derby Dam in 1906. The lake reached a historic low of about 3,784 feet in early 1967. The lake then rose about 8 feet as a result of the abnormally great runoff in 1969 and remained more or less stable during the 1970s because of changes in the Truckee River diversion management policy of the U.S. Department of the Interior. During the wet years of 1982-83, the lake level rose almost 20 feet. As awareness heightens over the cultural, biological, and scenic heritage of desert lakes such as Pyramid, Walker, and Mono, water laws are being changed to protect these treasures and the diverse life they support.

4.6 Note the large tufa deposit on the left.

5.1 Truckee River delta on the right.

On the left, just above the level of the road, note the white band of calcium carbonate deposited on the rocks. This white band is present around the lake at about the same elevation (3,872 feet), but the width varies. It represents some natural equilibrium level of the lake. Frémont noted this white zone in 1844, when it was only about 12 feet above lake level. A similar zone occurs around Winnemucca (dry) Lake, except that it is about 15 feet lower in elevation. Pyramid Lake rose above this white line three times between 1860 and 1900.

The Guanomi mine is on the left beyond the white band. It was developed in the 1920s as a gold-silver prospect, and explored in the 1930s for copper and molybdenum. The primary sulfide minerals, abundant pyrite and minor molybdenite, occur both as dissemination and in veinlets in the highly altered intrusive host rock, a quartz monzonite porphyry stock (after Bonham and Papke, 1969).

5.3 Turn off to Popcorn Rock on the right. The spheroidal form consists of concentric layers of thinolite tufa. Coralline tufa has been deposited on the surface.

The alignment of tufa domes and mounds along fractures that parallel the trend of young (late Quaternary) faults here and at other localities around the lake basin suggests that the Walker Lane fault zone was active and the focus of spring discharge (at least partly thermal) during Lake Lahontan time (Born, 1972). Known active geothermal areas at Pyramid Lake include The Needle Rocks on the north end of the lake (three geothermal wells were drilled there in the 1960s), the Pyramid, and a hot spring on Anaho Island.

Guanomi mine.

176

Anaho Island (left) and the Pyramid (right) from Popcorn Rock (foreground).

This stop also marks the former extent of the modern Truckee River delta during the lake's lowest historic stand in 1967. At that time, the river was rapidly cutting down into and laterally eroding the freshly exposed lake deposits, particularly during periods of high river flow. The intense erosion formed a large, prograding fluvial delta over the top of deeper-water lake sediments. For miles along the beaches in this area, similar complex sedimentary relationships revealing Pyramid Lake's dynamic past can be seen in vertical cross section in the low cliffs just above water level.

7.0 Across the lake at 1:00 is a good view of Anaho Island and the Pyramid. In the distance at 12:00 The Needle Rocks can be seen jutting above the shoreline.

The color of Pyramid Lake changes constantly. Generally this occurs because of changing intensity and angle of sunlight on suspended inorganic particles. But the most spectacular hues develop in late summer when the algae and tiny animals (mostly crustaceans) greatly increase their numbers forming blankets in the upper layers of the water. The wind mixes this plankton layer with the deeper waters, creating striking green to turquoise hues that contrast with the changing pastels of the surrounding desert ranges.

10.4 Spring flooding down this unnamed arroyo periodically washes out the road.

11.5 Turn off to the right for a closer look at the Indian Head mound.

Indian Head.

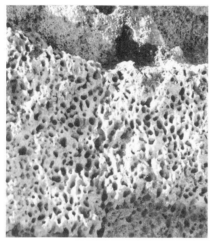

Coralline (dendritic) tufa.

Thinolite tufa.

Thinolite crystal.

178

11.7 **Turn around and return to the paved road.** Strandlines of Lake Lahontan are straight ahead on the slopes of the Pah Rah Range.

11.9 **Turn right on the paved road.**

12.9 Crossing the arroyo of Mullen Creek.

13.6 **Junction with State Route 445, on the left.**

You may continue straight ahead to access services and a museum at Sutcliffe or visit The Needle Rocks (see map on page 171) before returning to this point to resume the roadlog. Activities here at the lake include boating, fishing, waterskiing, swimming, hiking and exploring, and enjoying over 70 miles of sandy beaches. Be careful to drive only on roads; many cars have become stuck in soft beach sand.

0.0 **Reset odometer to 0.0 and turn left on State Route 445 (Pyramid Lake Highway) toward Sparks and Reno.**

0.2 **Carefully turn off on the left side of the road** for a final panoramic view of Pyramid Lake.

Today, Pyramid Lake is approximately 26 miles long, 4 to 11 miles wide, and up to 350 feet deep (just north of the Pyramid). Geologically, it occupies the depression near the northern end of the Walker Lane fault zone. Coincident with basin formation was uplift of the Lake Range on the east and the Virginia Mountains on the west. Major uplift was due to faulting.

Anaho, the large tufa-encrusted island directly east across the lake, has an elevation of 4,377 feet and was submerged when Lake Lahontan was at its maximum. In 1913, the 248-acre island was set aside as a National Wildlife Refuge by President Woodrow Wilson. It is the largest of seven American white pelican nesting colonies in North America. Sharing the island's approximately 750 acres (the lake level has declined to expose more land area) with the pelicans are double-crested cormorants, California gulls, Caspian terns, and great blue herons. The total summertime population of water birds can reach up to 16,000. The island is separated from the eastern shore of the lake by a moat of shallow water, which threatens to become a land bridge if the lake level drops more.

Pelican

The Pyramid (1925).

The Pyramid, which gave Frémont the idea for naming the lake when he first observed it in 1844, is the small pyramid-shaped tufa island to the left of Anaho Island.

From this vantage point it is easy to imagine Frémont's surprise at coming upon this vast expanse of water. He and his party of 24 men were traveling south from the Columbia River exploring the Great Basin before returning to the East, when they arrived at a pass on the north end of the lake. Captain Frémont's log for January 10, 1844 reads: "...beyond, a defile between the mountains descended rapidly about 2,000 feet; and, filling up all the lower space, was a sheet of green water, some twenty miles broad. It broke upon our eyes like the ocean. The neighboring peaks rose high above us, and we ascended one of them to obtain a better view. The waves were curling on the breeze, and their dark green color showed it to be a body of deep water. For a long time we sat enjoying the view, for we had become fatigued with mountains, and the free expanse of moving waves was very grateful. It was set like a gem in the mountains, which, from our position, seemed to enclose it almost entirely..."

For the next few days he made notes of the herds of mountain sheep, the salinity of the water, the tufa deposits, local geography, and the curious natives, who so generously supplied Frémont's men with the delicious "salmon-trout." On January 14th, Frémont named the lake: "... we camped on the shore, opposite a very remarkable rock in the lake, which had attracted our attention for many miles. It rose, according to our estimate, 600 feet above the water, and, from the point we viewed it, presented a pretty exact outline of the great pyramid of Cheops. Like other rocks along the shore, it seemed to be encrusted with calcareous cement. This striking feature suggested a name for the lake, and I called it Pyramid Lake..."

0.8 Carefully turn off the road on the left at the historical marker.

Here at the summit of Mullen Gap, one can see a Lake Lahontan terrace that was etched into rock (look behind the historical marker at a gray, rocky, horizontal band located about midway up the mountain). Note that the yellow-green lichen covering the rocks is found almost exclusively above the terrace level.

Below, Mullen Creek served as a waterway for Lake Lahontan waters. During high lake stands, lake water flowed westward into Warm Springs Valley, the western extent of Lahontan in this area. Note the large, sandy, table-like deposits of old lake sediments extending from the mouth of Mullen Creek toward Pyramid Lake.

1.1 For the next 4 miles the route follows Mullen Pass, an east-northeast-trending structural lineament separating the Virginia Mountains on

Arroyo of Mullen Creek. Eroded sediments from upstream are being deposited as a delta in Pyramid Lake. Note the Lahontan strandlines on the hills in the background.

Thinolite terrace of Lake Lahontan.

the north (right) and the Pah Rah Range on the south (left). Note the numerous Miocene dacite porphyry plugs and stocks standing as monoliths on the left and right for the next several miles. They have been dated at 20 million years old.

Volcanic rocks in the Virginia Mountains.

White sedimentary rocks contain Pliocene fossils situated below basalt flows in the Virginia Mountains.

Some of the Pyramid flora fossil plants found in Miocene diatomite deposits of the Mullen Pass area.

The Virginia Mountains are a northwest-trending block bounded on the northeast and southwest by northwest-trending faults of the Walker Lane. Faults with the same orientation occur within the range. Rocks in the southern quarter of the range are late Oligocene-early Miocene rhyolitic ash-flow tuffs and Miocene basalt flows, mudflows, agglomerates, tuffs, associated intrusive rocks, and some freshwater fossiliferous sedimentary rocks (diatomite, with some thin sandstone and shale). The ash-flow tuffs are varicolored, in white, bright red, and yellow produced by oxidation of the iron-bearing minerals in them.

1.7 Gas station and store on right.

The Pah Rah Range (on the left) is complexly faulted. Here, its northern portion exhibits the northwest-trending fault pattern of the Walker Lane. The rocks are late Oligocene to early Miocene rhyolitic ash-flow tuff and Miocene basalt and andesite flows.

Exposures of white Miocene diatomite crop out on the north side of the route at the base of the volcanic flows, stocks, and necks. The fossil remains of seeds and leaves of fir, pine, and spruce as well as such broad-leafed species as madrone, tan oak, mountain mahogany, alder, buckeye, birch, and maple are part of the Pyramid Flora of Axelrod (1992). Fifty to 70 species can be found in deposits of only a few square feet in areal extent. These plant parts were probably transported by streams from upstream forests. A modern area for like vegetation types and climate would be the Yuba River drainage in the Sierra Nevada of California; however, only 20 species in the Yuba River area have close allies in the Pyramid flora (after Axelrod, 1992).

4.5 Mine workings of the Pyramid mining district can be seen in the hills in the left foreground. Claims were located here as early as 1863, and the district was organized in 1866. Gold and silver ore assayed from $10 to $1,000 per ton, but little production occurred prior to 1878, when the Jones-Kincaid and the Monarch became the principal properties. Between 1881 and 1889 the Franco-American (Blondin) mine produced $87,000 in gold, silver, and copper. Mining was intermittent and small scale after that time. In 1954 uranium was discovered in the district. Many claims were staked and a little production was reported in 1955 and 1966.

The copper-lead-zinc-silver deposits of the district occur in northwest-trending veins in late Oligocene-early Miocene rhyolitic ash-flow tuffs. The ore is composed of the minerals pyrite, enargite, barite, galena, and sphalerite in a gangue of calcite, quartz and altered tuff. Little gold is present (usually less than 0.05 ounces per ton). The uranium occurs in generally northeast-trending fault zones and commonly localized along diabase dikes which intrude the ash-flow tuffs (after Bonham and Papke, 1969).

6.3 Winnemucca Valley is off to the right at 2:00.

7.4 Entering Warm Springs Valley (recently the name Palomino Valley has also been applied). This valley is a down-dropped block bounded by northwest-trending faults of the Walker Lane. The valley fill, composed of Pliocene and younger (including Lake Lahonton) sedimentary rocks, ranges in depth from 2,000 to 3,400 feet.

The rocks on the right are Cretaceous granite, granodiorite, and quartz diorite. Rocks on the left are complexly faulted late Oligocene

BLM National Wild Horse and Burro Center at Palomino Valley.

to early Miocene ash-flow tuffs which overlie the Cretaceous intrusive rocks.

Mesozoic basement rocks crop out extensively in this area southwest of the Walker Lane boundary faults. They have been displaced upward at least 3,000 feet relative to the Mesozoic rocks in the Virginia Mountains block.

Erosional remnants of Tertiary rocks indicate that this area was formerly covered by some of the same Tertiary rock units that cover the Virginia Mountains-Pah Rah Range block. Uplift occurred here after deposition of the late Oligocene-early Miocene ash-flow tuffs and prior to the eruption of late Miocene volcanic rocks.

11.0 The Bureau of Land Management National Wild Horse and Burro Placement Center at Palomino Valley is on the left.

Nevada is home to most of the nation's wild horses and burros. In 1994, there were about 23,000 wild horses and burros in the state, mostly in herd management areas on public lands administered by the BLM. Early explorers' journals indicate that horses were in northern Nevada by the 1820s, apparently abandoned by Indians. As the cavalry, ranchers, or miners demanded horses, many were trapped and trained. Horses and burros were first brought to the New World by early Spanish explorers.

In 1971, Congress passed the Wild Free-Roaming Horse and Burro Act to protect, manage, and control wild horses and burros on public land. These animals were declared to be "living symbols of the historic and pioneer spirit of the West." To control the overpopulation of wild horses and burros in certain areas, excess animals are gathered and transported to placement centers like the Palomino Valley facility for adoption by the public

With few exceptions, excess Nevada wild horses and burros are brought to this facility where they are readied for adoption (vaccinations, identification numbers, age determination). Among the adopters are the U.S. Marine Corps Mounted Color Guard, often seen in parades and horse shows.

14.2 The route passes through Bacon Rind Flat. On the left, late Oligocene-early Miocene ash-flow tuffs crop out on both sides of Rattlesnake Canyon.

Hungry Ridge on the right is composed of Cretaceous(?) plutonic rocks overlain by late Oligocene-early Miocene ash-flow tuffs. The ridge is separated from the valley by a major north-northeast fault parallel to the highway you are traveling. The ash-flow tuff that caps the ridge is faulted down to form the shoulder of the ridge and to underlie the valley here. North-northeast and west to northwest-trending faults offset the rocks.

15.6 Axehandle Road intersection.

Sugarloaf Peak looking east.

The Wedekind mine.

16.3 Entering Spanish Springs Valley. Straight ahead on the skyline is Slide Mountain. Mount Rose is the higher peak on the right. Both are in the Carson Range.

17.6 At the base of the hills at 2:00, light-gray decomposed granite is mined for use mainly as fill or "borrow" material. The present pit is operated for crushed stone (Cretaceous quartz diorite) for use in aggregate base and as asphalt and concrete aggregate. Cretaceous(?) granite continues to crop out in the hills to the right, along with pre-Lake Lahontan terrace, alluvial fan and pediment gravels, and lake deposits. These deposits are also found along the entire western margin of the Truckee Meadows (to the south).

18.5 On the left at 10:00 is Sugarloaf Peak. It is composed of Miocene andesitic basalt, overlying Cretaceous granite. The visible surface of the Pah Rah Range in the distance is composed of late Miocene basalt.

  The meadows of Spanish Springs Valley are kept green with irrigation water diverted by the Orr Ditch from the Truckee River. Springs kept this area marshy in the 1930s and 1940s before development began.

22.4 Spanish Springs Road intersection. The Truckee Meadows are straight ahead. The route is passing through the Wedekind mining district. Note the adits and dumps on the hills to the right.

  George Wedekind was a piano tuner and weekend prospector who established his Wedekind mine in 1896. He produced about

$100,000 from this mine before selling out to Governor John Sparks for $175,000. By 1901, about 50 shafts were sunk in the area and this marked the main period of production with anywhere from $107,091 (official production records) to $229,621 (unofficial smelter figures) in gold and silver being produced. The surface ores reportedly contained rich silver chloride, some gold, cerussite, and anglesite (Bonham and Papke, 1969). In 1903, a large body of hot acid water was struck 213 feet down that made mining difficult. Mining was also unprofitable because the mill was designed for the surface oxide ore and not the sulfide ore that was mined at depth. Mining for lead, zinc, and silver oxides from 200 to 400 feet down was attempted again in the 1920s and 1930s, but the district has been inactive since then.

Cretaceous(?) granodiorite crops out on the north end of the district, but Miocene andesite flows are the major rock unit exposed in the area. The flows are highly altered and have undergone extensive acid sulfate hydrothermal alteration similar to that along the Geiger Grade (refer to page 43). Mineralization occurs as stockworks in northwest- and north-trending fracture zones.

As residential housing spread into this mining area, several surprise cave-ins affected structures built too close to old shafts. The clay-rich hydrothermally altered rock also causes structural problems for homes. **Remember: "Stay out and stay alive" is a good motto when tempted to explore old mines.**

28.3 Cross Queen Way. Entering the City of Sparks. Continue straight ahead on State Route 445 to I-80.

28.6 Crossing North McCarran Blvd.

30.1 Turn right on the on-ramp to I-80 West to return to Reno.

33.3 Virginia Street exit from I-80 and end of Trip D.

GLOSSARY

accessory mineral A mineral that occurs in a rock in relatively small quantities.

adit A horizontal or nearly horizontal passage from the surface into a mine.

agglomerate A pyroclastic rock containing a preponderance of rounded or suban-gular fragments greater than 32 mm.

alloformation Mappable body of sedimentary rock that is defined and identified by discontinuities that bound it. For Quaternary alluvial units, these boundaries are soils or geomorphic surfaces.

alluvial Pertaining to alluvium.

alluvial fan A fan-shaped deposit of alluvium typically built where a stream leaves a steep mountain valley and runs out onto a lower-gradient surface.

alluvium Sediment deposited by streams in nonmarine environments, including river beds, floodplains, deltas, and fans at the base of mountain slopes.

alteration *See altered, hydrothermal alteration.*

altered Said of a rock that has undergone a change in its mineral composition, typically brought about by the action of hydrothermal solutions.

alumina Aluminum oxide.

alunite A mineral (hydrated potassium aluminum sulfate), found usually in soft white, gray, or pink masses in hydrothermally altered rocks that originally contained abundant feldspar.

alunitization Introduction of, or replacement by, alunite.

amorphous Said of a mineral or other substance that lacks crystalline structure.

andesite A fine-grained volcanic rock that solidifies from molten lava at the Earth's surface. It is intermediate in composition between basalt and rhyolite, and ranges in color from dark gray-green, to lighter gray, red, or brown.

anglesite A mineral, lead sulfate.

antecedent valley A valley that was established before tectonic uplift occurred.

aphanitic Rock texture in which the individual minerals are too small to be distinguished with the unaided eye.

arrastra A primitive form of grinding mill that consists of a rock lined pit in which ore is crushed by stones that are attached by poles to a central pillar and dragged around the pit.

ash, volcanic Fine pyroclastic material produced by the explosive emission of hot, gas-charged lava from a volcanic crater or fissure that cools on its descent to the ground surface. It consists of fragments under 4 mm in diameter and is usually light gray.

ash-flow tuff Pyroclastic volcanic rock composed of formerly gas-charged volcanic ash that flowed as a "fiery cloud" down the side of a volcano or erupted from a caldera.

asthenosphere The weak, plastic, partly molten layer of the upper mantle directly below the lithosphere. It lies at a depth of 100 to 350 km (60 to 220 miles) below the Earth's surface.

basalt A fine-grained igneous rock that solidified from molten lava at the Earth's surface. It is usually black or dark gray, due to the predominance of the minerals calcic plagioclase, olivine, pyroxene, and other dark-colored accessory minerals. It may have cavities (vesicles) that formed by trapped gas as the magma cooled.

basaltic andesite An igneous rock intermediate in composition between andesite and basalt. Its color is commonly darker than andesite and lighter than basalt.

basement The undifferentiated complex of rocks (generally igneous or metamorphic) that underlie surface rocks.

Basin and Range province A physiographic region in the western United States that consists of fault-block mountains and intervening sediment-filled basins.

basin-and-range extension Extension, or pulling apart, of the crust of the Earth in the western United States that has produced the present physiography of generally north-trending mountain ranges separated by intervening sediment-filled basins.

basin-and-range-type faults Faults, generally moderately steep and normal, that result from basin and range extension and produce the typical graben and horst structural style. Thus, major faults of this type bound the mountain blocks (horsts).

batholith A large body of intrusive igneous (plutonic) rock generally having an area of over 40 square miles. They are commonly produced by multiple intrusions.

bedding Depositional layers or planes dividing sedimentary rocks of the same or different lithology.

bedrock Solid rock exposed at the Earth's surface or overlain by unconsolidated material.

biotite A common rock-forming mineral and a member of the mica group of minerals. It ranges from dark brown to green and exhibits perfect basal cleavage, that is, it will peel into thin, nearly transparent layers along one plane.

bleaching A lightening of the original color of rock; a surface effect caused by long exposure to weathering (including acid solutions) or a more penetrating effect caused when circulating solutions, generally hot, have altered the original chemical composition of the minerals forming the rocks.

bornite A mineral (copper iron sulfide). Also known as peacock copper ore, it is characterized by an iridescent purple color on tarnished or weathered surfaces. A fresh fracture is red-brown.

brackish Salty, generally less so than sea water, usually defined as less than 15 to 30 parts per thousand salinity.

breccia A coarse-grained rock composed of angular fragments of broken rock in a finer-grained matrix.

brecciated Rock that has been broken into angular fragments within a finer-grained matrix which may or may not cement the angular fragments.

calcite Calcium carbonate, the principal constituent of limestone.

caldera A large, bowl-shaped volcanic depression with a diameter many times greater than the included volcanic vent or vents. It may be formed by explosion or collapse.

carbon-14 dating See radiocarbon dating.

chalcedony Cryptocrystalline quartz and much chert, commonly microscopically fibrous. The material of agate.

cerussite A mineral (lead carbonate). An ore of lead.

chalcopyrite A mineral (copper iron sulfide). An ore of copper.

chlorite A mineral group consisting of hydrous silicates of aluminum, ferrous iron, and magnesium that are closely related to the micas. Chlorite has platy cleavage and is generally greenish.

cinder, volcanic Uncemented, glassy, vesicular rock ejected from a volcanic vent.

cinder cone A conical hill formed by the accumulation of volcanic ash or cinders (generally of basalt composition) around a vent.

clast A piece of broken rock or an individual constituent of sedimentary rock produced by the physical disintegration of a larger rock mass.

clastic rocks Rocks consisting of clasts or fragments of other rocks that have moved individually from their place of origin.

clay 1. An extremely fine-grained, natural sediment or soft rock composed of clay-sized (less than 0.002 mm) particles. 2. A group of silicate minerals that generally occur as platy particles in fine aggregates.

colluvium A general term applied to loose and incoherent deposits usually at the foot of a slope or cliff and brought there chiefly by gravity. Talus and cliff debris are included in such deposits.

composite volcano A volcano that emits both fragmental material and viscous lava, and that builds up a large steep conical cone (examples are peaks in the Cascade Range). Also called a stratovolcano.

conglomerate A sedimentary rock consisting of rounded rock fragments, over 2 mm in diameter, set in a finer-grained matrix.

conjugate fractures or joints Two sets of fractures or joints that either have the same strike, but dip in opposite directions (and intersect at a high angle) or that dip steeply and intersect at a high angle.

contact The place or surface where two different kinds of rocks come together.

continental plate A plate or slab of the Earth's crust that consists partly or mainly of continental crust.

continental crust The portion of the Earth's crust that underlies the continents and is relatively enriched in silica and alumina. *See oceanic crust.*

coralline Resembling coral. Coralline tufa resembles marine "brain coral."

corestone The central, hard rounded core of rock that still remains intact as the outer surface is weathered into smaller fragments of rock and constituent minerals. Produced by spheroidal weathering following rock disintegration along joints.

country rock *See wall rock.*

crop out *See outcrop.*

crossbeds A sequence of beds in granular sediments that are inclined at an angle to the main bedding planes. In plan view, the inclined beds are at right-angles to the direction of the wind or water current that deposited them.

crust The outermost compositional shell of the Earth, 10 to 40 km (6 to 24 miles) thick, consisting mainly of relatively low density silicate rocks.

crustal extension Separation, or pulling apart, of the Earth's crust due to forces in the lower crust and mantle, such as convention currents, which are believed to move the continental and oceanic plates of the Earth's crust. This process is often accompanied by increased heat production and broad uparching of the Earth's surface.

cryptocrystalline Crystalline, but so fine grained that the individual mineral components cannot be seen with an ordinary microscope.

cyanidation A process involving the use of cyanide (potassium or sodium cyanide), especially in the recovery of gold and silver from ore.

cyanobacteria Formerly called blue-green algae; cyano is Greek for blue.

dacite A light-colored volcanic rock about midway between andesite and rhyolite in mineralogical composition and appearance.

debris flow The downslope movement of a mass of unconsolidated and unsorted rock with associated water and mud.

dendritic Treelike; branching in form.

diabase A medium grained, intrusive igneous rock that is the fine grained equivalent of basalt. The predominate mineral is plagioclase feldspar along with olivine and pyroxene; quartz is absent.

diatomaceous earth A friable earthy deposit composed of nearly pure silica and consisting essentially of the frustules (skeletons) of the microscopic plants called diatoms.

diatomite The rock name for the consolidated equivalent of diatomaceous earth.

dike A tabular sheet of intrusive igneous rock that cuts across the structure of the intruded rock or cuts massive rock.

dip The angle in degrees between the horizontal and an inclined geologic plane, such as a bedding plane or a fault. Dip is measured in a plane that is perpendicular to the intersection of the plane with the horizontal.

dip-slip The component of fault movement that is parallel with the fault dip.

diorite A plutonic (intrusive) igneous rock composed essentially of sodium plagioclase and hornblende, biotite, or pyroxene. Small amounts of quartz and orthoclase may be present.

downthrown block Block of the Earth's crust that has moved relatively downward along a normal fault.

downwarped Gentle bending of the Earth's crust downward without forming pronounced folds or dislocations.

enargite A mineral, copper arsenic sulfide. An ore of copper.

en echelon A term describing geologic features, especially faults, that are in an overlapping or staggered parallel arrangement in a linear zone.

eolian Formed by, or related to wind action.

epithermal A term applied to those ore deposits formed in and along fissures or other openings in rocks by deposition at shallow depths from ascending hot solutions. They are distinguished from mesothermal and hypothermal lodes by the minerals they contain, by their textures, and by the character of the alteration of their wall rocks.

erosion The group of related processes by which rock is broken down physically and chemically and the products removed from any part of the Earth's surface. It includes the processes of weathering, solution, and transportation.

escarpment A long, generally continuous cliff or steep face at the edge of a region of high local relief.

evaporite A rock formed by the evaporation of water in a restricted basin; also, the minerals of such deposits.

exfoliation The breaking off or peeling off of concentric sheets of rock from the bare outer rock surfaces of larger rock masses by the action of either physical or chemical forces.

extension In geology, horizontal expansion or pulling apart of the Earth's crust.

extrusive igneous rocks *See volcanic rocks.*

fan *See alluvial fan.*

fault A fracture or planar break in rock (which may be a few centimeters or many kilometers long) along which there has been movement of one side relative to the other.

fault-block mountains Mountains bounded on at least two opposite sides by faults. Common in the Basin and Range province.

fault controlled Features (especially geographic or geomorphic) on or near the Earth's surface which have developed along or been formed by faults. Such features include streams, ponds, mountain ranges, escarpments, and ore zones.

fault scarp The steep slope or cliff formed by a fault. Most fault scarps have been modified by erosion since the faulting.

fault surface The surface along which movement has taken place.

fault trace The line of intersection of a fault plane with the Earth's surface.

fault zone A fault, instead of being a single clean fracture, may be a zone as much as hundreds or even thousands of feet wide; the fault zone consists of numerous interlacing small faults or a complex zone of fault gouge or breccia.

feldspar A framework silicate mineral common in many rocks and making up 60 percent of the Earth's crust. Includes plagioclase and sanidine.

ferricrete Sand and gravel that is more or less cemented with iron oxide, and often stained rusty red.

floodplain That portion of a river valley that is covered with water when the river overflows its banks at flood stages.

flotation A method of mineral separation (especially for ores) whereby a froth created in water by a variety of chemicals will float some finely crushed minerals, and allow others to sink.

fluvial Of or pertaining to streams or rivers, especially erosional and depositional processes of streams and the sediments and landforms resulting from them.

footwall The lower side of a fault plane, vein, lode, or bed of ore. So named because miners in underground developments along a vein stood on the "foot" wall. *See hanging wall.*

formation A body of rock distinctive enough on the basis of physical properties and of sufficient extent to constitute a basic unit for a geologic map.

gabbro A dark colored plutonic igneous rock consisting of calcic plagioclase and pyroxene and olivine. Magnetite or ilmenite are common accessory minerals.

gabion A cylinder of metal, wire mesh, or wicker filled with stones or earth, and used in building fortifications, dams, foundations, and erosion control structures.

gangue The nonmetalliferous or nonvaluable minerals in ore. Quartz and calcite are common gangue minerals.

geomorphology The science that deals with the form of the Earth, the general configuration of its surface, and the changes that take place in the evolution of landforms.

geothermal Related to the heat of the Earth's interior; geothermal power involves extraction of that heat through circulating subsurface water.

glacial Pertaining to, characteristic of, produced or deposited by, or derived from a glacier.

gouge A thin layer of soft, earthy, putty-like rock material along a fault or wall of a vein.

graben A block of the Earth's crust, generally long compared to its width, that has been downthrown along faults relative to the rocks on either side.

granite A light-colored coarse-grained, igneous (plutonic) rock containing the minerals quartz and alkali feldspar, with lesser amounts of plagioclase and mica.

granitic rock Granite or a close relative, such as granodiorite or quartz monzonite.

granodiorite A coarse-grained, plutonic rock resembling granite and consisting of quartz, plagioclase, and potassium feldspar, with biotite mica, hornblende, or pyroxene as the mafic (dark colored) minerals. The almost equal amounts of dark and light-colored minerals give this rock a salt-and-pepper appearance.

groundmass The finer-grained mineral material between the phenocrysts (large crystals) in a porphyritic igneous rock.

grus A coarse sand consisting of the fragmental products of the decomposition of granite by weathering at the Earth's surface.

gypsite (gypsum) A rock composed chiefly of gypsum, a mineral (hydrous calcium sulfate). A common evaporite mineral, used in the manufacture of wallboard.

hanging wall The rock on the upper side of a fault, mineral vein, or mineral deposit. *See footwall.*

headframe The structure above a mine shaft supporting the pulley over which the hoisting cable passes.

Holocene Recent geologic time (10,000 years ago to the present).

hornblende A common rock-forming dark silicate mineral with a complex chemical formula.

horst An elongate fault block that has been uplifted along faults relative to the adjacent rocks.

hydrothermal Literally, "hot water"; describes processes or ore deposits related to circulating subsurface water warmed by shallow magma or hot rock; hydrothermal fluids commonly contain dissolved minerals and gasses.

hydrothermal alteration Changes in rocks brought about by the addition or removal of materials through the medium of hydrothermal fluids; silicification, for example.

hydrous Said of a mineral compound containing water.

igneous rock Rock formed by the cooling and consolidation of magma.

illite A group of clay minerals intermediate in composition between muscovite and montmorillonite.

ilmenite A black mineral, iron titanium oxide. A common accessory mineral in igneous rocks.

interbedded Interstratified. Occurring between or alternating with beds of a different material.

intrusive igneous rock Rock emplaced as magma into preexisting rock below the Earth's surface. *See plutonic.*

intrusives Intrusive igneous rocks.

joint A fracture in rock along which no appreciable displacement has occurred.

jokulhlaup An Icelandic term for a catastrophic flood that results from the sudden release of a large amount of water from behind a glacial ice dam.

lacustrine Pertaining to, produced by, or formed in a lake.

lahar A volcanic mudflow deposit.

landform Any feature of the Earth's surface having a characteristic shape as the product of natural processes. Examples are continents, ocean basins, mountains, alluvial fans, sand dunes, and valleys.

landslide A general term covering a variety of rapid, mass movement processes downslope on the Earth's surface.

latite An extrusive (volcanic) igneous rock in which potassium feldspar and plagioclase are present in nearly equal amounts. Augite and hornblende are usually present and biotite may be present.

lava flow Magma that flows out of the Earth's surface.

left-lateral fault A strike-slip fault in which relative motion is such that to an observer looking directly at (perpendicular to) the fault, the motion of the block on the opposite side of the fault is to the left. *See page 10.*

lichen Mosslike plants consisting of algae and fungi growing in close association in patches on rocks and trees.

life zone A zone defined by a characteristic assemblage of plants.

limestone A sedimentary rock consisting chiefly of calcium carbonate, mainly in the form of the mineral calcite.

lineament A topographic line that is structurally controlled. Significant lines in the landscape that reveal the hidden architecture of the bedrock.

lithoid Stonelike. A dense and fine-grained type of tufa.

lithology The description of compositional and physical characteristics of a rock.

lithosphere The rigid, outermost layer of the Earth, 50 to 200 km (30 to 120 miles) thick, encompassing the crust and upper mantle.

Ma Million years old or million years ago (mega-annum).

mafic A dark-colored rock, magma, or mineral rich in iron and magnesium.

magnesia Magnesium oxide.

magma Molten rock (together with any suspended crystals and dissolved gases) in the mantle or crust. Igneous rocks are formed when magma cools and consolidates.

magma chamber A reservoir in the Earth's crust occupied by magma.

magmatic Of, pertaining to, or derived from magma.

magnetite Magnetic iron ore. A black mineral (iron oxide). A frequent minor accessory mineral of igneous rocks.

Mesozoic One of the large division or eras of geologic time, following the Paleozoic Era and succeeded by the Cenozoic Era, comprising the Triassic, Jurassic and Cretaceous Periods. *See page 13.*

metadacite Metamorphosed dacite.

metamorphic rock Rock whose original textures or mineral components, or both, have been transformed to new textures and components as a result of one or several of the following: high temperatures, high pressure, and chemically active fluids.

metastibnite An amorphous (noncrystalline) brick red deposit of antimony trisulfide; the crystalline form is the mineral stibnite.

metavolcanic Metamorphosed volcanic rocks.

mica A rock-forming silicate mineral having a platy or scaly form; muscovite and biotite are micas.

mineral A naturally occurring, inorganic, crystalline, solid element or compound with a definite composition or compositional range and a regular internal structure.

Miocene The fourth of the five epochs into which the Tertiary Period is divided. *See page 13.*

montmorillonite A group of clay minerals (general formula is hydrated aluminum silicate). They are characterized by swelling in water.

monzonite A granular plutonic rock resembling granite that contains approximately equal amounts of orthoclase and plagioclase. Quartz is usually present, but comprises 2 percent or less of the rock's volume. Hornblende and biotite are usually present along with several accessory minerals.

moraine A mound, ridge, or other accumulation of unsorted and unstratified sediment and larger clasts of rock deposited by a glacier. For example, an end moraine is one produced at the front of a glacier. *See page 120.*

mudflow A flow of a mixture of mud and water.

mudstone A rock that includes clay, silt, siltstone, claystone, shale, and argillite. The term is used when precise rock identification is in doubt or when a deposit consists of an indefinite or variable mixture of clay, silt, and sand particles.

muscovite A potassium aluminum silicate mineral of the mica family.

neck *See volcanic neck.*

normal fault An inclined fault along which the upper side has moved downward relative to the lower side. *See page 10.*

oceanic plate A tectonic plate of the Earth's crust that underlies an ocean.

oceanic crust That type of Earth's crust that underlies the ocean basins. It is relatively enriched in silica and magnesia. *See continental crust.*

olivine A magnesium-iron silicate mineral which commonly occurs as phenocrysts in basalt.

opal An amorphous mineral (or mineral gel), hydrated silica.

opaline Having the mineralogy and physical characteristics of opal.

ore The naturally occurring material from which a mineral or minerals of economic value can be extracted.

orebody Generally a solid and fairly continuous mass of ore which can be distinguished by form or character from adjoining country rock.

orthoclase A mineral (potassium aluminum silicate), a member of the feldspar group and a common mineral in granitic rocks. Its luster is glassy, and it ranges in color from colorless to white, gray, or pink.

outcrop That part of a geologic formation that appears at the surface of the Earth.

outwash Stratified sand and gravel deposited by meltwater streams beyond active glacial ice.

oxidation The process of combining with oxygen. The removal of one or more electrons from an ion or an atom.

pediment An eroded bedrock surface that slopes away from the base of mountains in arid regions and is thinly or discontinuously covered by alluvium.

pegmatite A very coarse-grained igneous rock, generally containing the same minerals as granite, that commonly occurs as dikes.

petroglyph Writings or drawings chipped or scraped into rock surfaces or faces. Usually the markings are made in the veneer of dark rock varnish, exposing underlying lighter-colored rock for good visual contrast.

phenocryst One of the larger, isolated crystals in a porphyritic igneous rock.

phragmite A type of reed that grows in wet areas.

physiographic Pertaining to the surface features and landforms of the Earth.

plagioclase A feldspar mineral group (aluminum silicate with variable amounts of calcium and sodium), whose members comprise some of the most common rock-forming minerals. Plagioclase luster is glassy to pearly, and its color ranges from colorless to white, to gray, to yellowish and flesh-red.

plate tectonics The processes or mechanisms by which the Earth's lithosphere (upper crust) is broken up into a series of rigid plates that move over the asthenosphere (lower crust, upper mantle). *See page 11*

playa The flat, vegetation-free, lowermost area of a desert basin, where water gathers after a rain and is evaporated.

Pleistocene The earlier of the two epochs in the Quaternary Period. *See page 13.*

plexus An interwoven arrangement of parts; a network.

Pliocene The last epoch in the Tertiary Period. *See page 13.*

plug *See volcanic plug.*

pluton A body of igneous rock that formed at considerable depth beneath the Earth's surface by consolidation of magma.

plutonic rock Magma that penetrated into or between other rocks and solidified at relatively great depth below the Earth's surface. Intrusive rock emplaced at depths below volcanic processes.

pluvial lake A lake formed during a period of higher precipitation and stream runoff, especially during Pleistocene glacial periods.

porphyritic Term applied to igneous rock that has coarse crystals (phenocrysts) in a finely crystalline or glassy groundmass.

porphyry Igneous rock containing conspicuous phenocrysts in a fine-grained groundmass. The resulting texture is described as porphyritic.

potassium-argon dating A type of radiometric age dating using the known rate of decay of potassium-40 to argon-40.

potassium feldspar Refers mainly to the minerals orthoclase, sanidine, microcline or adularia, the feldspars rich in potassium.

pozzolan A number of natural and manufactured materials (ash, tuff, slag, etc.) which impart specific properties to cement, such as superior strength and resistance to saline and acidic solutions.

ppm Parts per million.

Precambrian All geologic time from the formation of the Earth to the start of the Paleozoic. More than 90 percent of the Earth's estimated 4.5 billion years is Precambrian.

prograding The outward extension of a shoreline into the sea or a lake due to sedimentation.

pyrite A brass yellow mineral (iron sulfide). Also called "fool's gold."

pyroclastic A general term applied to volcanic materials that have been explosively or aerially ejected from a volcanic vent. Also, a general term for the class of volcanic rocks made up of these materials, including volcanic ash. A volcanic rock texture; composed of fragments.

pyroxene A group of common silicate minerals (containing varying amounts of magnesium, iron, calcium, aluminum, and sodium) that are light green to black.

quartz monzonite A granular plutonic rock that resembles and is related to granite. Its major constituents are potassium feldspar, plagioclase and quartz, with minor quantities of biotite, hornblende, apatite, and zircon.

radiocarbon Radioactive carbon, especially the C^{14} isotope.

radiocarbon dating The determination of the age of a material by measuring the proportion of the isotope C^{14} (radiocarbon) in the carbon it contains. This method is suitable for the determination of ages up to a maximum of about 30,000 years.

rain shadow The region of diminished precipitation on the lee side of a mountain or mountain range, where the rain and snow are noticeably less than on the windward side.

rhyodacite The volcanic, fine-grained equivalent of a granodiorite.

rhyolite A fine-grained igneous (volcanic) rock with the same chemical composition as granite.

rhyolitic Having the characteristics of a rhyolite.

rift valley Valley produced by the subsidence of a strip bounded by two parallel normal faults.

right-lateral fault A strike-slip fault in which relative motion is such that to an observer looking directly at (perpendicular to) the fault, the motion of the block on the opposite side of the fault is to the right. *See page 10.*

riparian Of, relating to, or growing on the bank of a river, lake, or other water body.

rock Any naturally formed, solid aggregate of one or more minerals.

rock varnish A thin, dark, shiny coating consisting mainly of manganese and iron oxides, formed on the surfaces of stones and rock outcrops in various climatic regions (from hot deserts to glacial regions) after varying lengths or exposure.

roof pendant Older rocks "floating in" or projecting down from the roof into a batholith. On a geologic map the roof pendant is completely surrounded by the rocks of the batholith.

sag pond A pond occupying a depression along an active fault, formed where recent movement has impounded drainage.

sandstone A sedimentary rock made up of sand-sized particles.

sanidine A mineral, the high-temperature form of potassium feldspar, which occurs in volcanic rocks.

scabland Area of exposed rock surfaces with little soil or vegetation and deep, dry channels scoured into the surface. Commonly produced by glacial flood waters.

scarp *See fault scarp.*

sedimentary rock A consolidated accumulation of rock and mineral grains and organic matter or a rock formed by chemical or organic precipitation.

shale A very fine-grained, laminated, sedimentary rock made up of clay- and silt-sized particles. Shale tends to break along parallel planes.

sheared Highly deformed (crushed or stretched out) due to differential movement of rock bodies that have been forced to slide past each other along a plane or zone.

shear zone A zone in which shearing has occurred on a large scale so that the rock is crushed and brecciated.

shield volcano A volcano with a low, flat, broad shape formed by the build-up of many thin lava flows, usually of basalt.

silica Silicon dioxide.

silicate A chemical compound or mineral made up of silica tetrahedra, which are arranged with metal elements to form chains, sheets, or frameworks. Many common rock-forming minerals are silicates.

siliceous Containing abundant silica.

silicification The introduction of or replacement by silica. The silica formed is generally fine-grained quartz, chalcedony, or opal, and may both fill pores and replace existing minerals.

silt A sediment in which most of the particles are smaller than fine sand and larger than clay, generally between 0.002 and 0.05 mm in diameter.

siltstone A clastic sedimentary rock composed predominantly of silt-sized particles.

sinter A chemical sediment deposited by a hot spring. Usually the term refers to siliceous sinter, a deposit of amorphous silica. Calcareous spring deposits, of either hot or cold springs, are commonly called travertine. *See also tufa.*

slickensides Striated or highly polished surfaces on hard rocks produced by movement along a fault.

sorbed Absorbed. Taken in, soaked up, or assimilated.

spall To break off in layers parallel to a surface, as by exfoliation; or, the curved and sharp-edged piece of rock produced by this process.

sphene A calcium titanium silicate mineral, generally brown or yellow, that is found in small amounts in igneous rocks.

sphalerite A mineral (zinc iron sulfide). The principal ore of zinc.

spheroidal weathering The successive loosening of concentric shells of decayed rock from a solid rock mass as a result of weathering.

stibnite A mineral, antimony sulfide. The principal ore of antimony.

stock A body of intrusive (plutonic) rock that is similar to but smaller than a batholith, having a surface exposure of less than 40 square miles.

stockwork An ore deposit of such a form that it is worked in floors or stories. It may be a solid mass of ore, or a rock mass so interpenetrated by small veins of ore that the whole must be mined together.

stope An underground excavation from which ore has been extracted.

strandline Former shore or beach line, as around a lake.

strata Layers or tabular beds of sedimentary rock that consist of approximately the same kind of material throughout, and that are distinct from the layers above and below.

stratification The layered arrangement of sediments, sedimentary rocks, or extrusive igneous rocks.

striated Solid rock that has had parallel grooves cut into it during movement along fault planes or of glacial ice.

strike The direction, measured as an angle from true north, of a horizontal line in the plane of an inclined rock unit, joint, fault or other structural surface. It is perpendicular to the dip.

strike-slip fault A high-angle fault along which displacement has been horizontal. *See right-lateral strike-slip fault, left-lateral strike-slip fault, and page 10.*

subduction The process whereby a slab of oceanic lithosphere is descending beneath another plate (continental or oceanic) and carried down into the mantle of the Earth. *See page 11.*

subduction zone An elongate region on the Earth's surface where subduction is taking place. *See page 11.*

tabular Slab-like; having a table-like surface.

talus An accumulation of coarsely broken rock debris from rockfalls or slides that forms an apron sloping outward from the cliff supplying the material.

tectonic Of, or pertaining to, the rock structures and external forms resulting from the deformation of the Earth's crust.

tectonism Crustal instability.

thinolite A tufa deposit of calcium carbonate consisting of elongate, terminated crystal-like forms up to several inches long.

thrust fault A low-angle reverse fault with the fault plane dipping less than 45 degrees. *See page 10.*

tufa A chemical sedimentary rock composed of calcium carbonate, deposited from solution in the water of a spring or lake or from percolating ground water.

tuff A rock formed of compacted volcanic fragments. A general term for all consolidated pyroclastic rocks.

tule A large bulrush found in lakes and marshes.

unconformably Having the relation of unconformity to the underlying rocks. The overlying rocks did not succeed the underlying strata in immediate order of age and in parallel position.

unconformity A substantial gap or break in the geologic record. A surface within a sedimentary sequence that records a period of nondeposition or erosion.

understory The plants of a forest undergrowth.

upthrown block The block or mass of rock on that side of a fault which has been displaced relatively upward.

varved sediments 1. Sedimentary beds or laminations that are deposited within one year's time. 2. A pair of contrasting laminae representing seasonal sedimentation, as, summer (light) and winter (dark) within a single year.

vein A mineral-filled fault or fracture.

veinlet A narrow vein or occurrence of ore in rock or gangue. A thin filling or intrusion in rock.

vent The conduit or orifice through which volcanic materials (lava, gas, water vapor) reach the Earth's surface.

vesicular Containing holes or small openings (vesicles). Certain volcanic rocks contain vesicles resulting from gas trapped as the erupted lava cooled.

volcanic arc An elongate arc of volcanoes formed above an active subduction zone.

volcanic ash *See ash, volcanic.*

volcanic dome *See dome.*

volcaniclastic Said of rocks formed of fragments (clasts) derived from volcanic rocks.

volcanic neck The solidified material filling a vent or pipe of a volcano. The hard igneous rock may resist erosion better than the mountain mass originally encompassing it and eventually stand alone as a column, tower, or crag.

volcanic plug Necks consisting of a monolithic mass of solidified volcanic rock.

volcanic rock Igneous rocks derived from magma or magmatic materials that are poured out or ejected (extruded) at or very near the Earth's surface.

volcano A vent from which magma, gas, and ash are erupted; also, the usually conical structure built by such eruptions.

wall rock The rock forming the walls of a vein or lode; rock into which a pluton is intruded.

warping The gentle bending of the Earth's crust without forming pronounced folds or faults.

wash A shallow streambed with steep sides cut into unconsolidated sediments. This kind of streambed usually carries water only after brief, local precipitation.

waterlaid Refers to sediment deposited by water.

zircon A mineral, zirconium silicate. A common accessory mineral in siliceous igneous rocks.

BIBLIOGRAPHY

Alt, D.D., and Hyndman, D.W., 1975, Roadside geology of northern California: Mountain Press Publishing Company, Missoula, Montana, 244 p.

American Geological Institute, 1974, Dictionary of geological terms: Anchor Books, Anchor Press/Doubleday, Garden City, New York, 545 p.

Ansari, M.B., 1976, Comstock place names—the names of Storey County, Nevada: Camp Nevada Monograph 7, 59 p.

Ansari, M.B., 1989, Mines and mills of the Comstock region, western Nevada: Camp Nevada Monograph No. 8, 101 p.

Ashley, R.P., 1980, Geology of the Virginia Range, in Epithermal ore deposits of northwestern Nevada: U.S. Geological Survey and Society of Economic Geologists field conference, May 1980, Reno, Nevada, guidebook, p. 52-63.

Ashley, R.P., 1980, Roadlog—Steamboat Springs to U.S. Highway 50, in Epithermal ore deposits of northwestern Nevada: U.S. Geological Survey and Society of Economic Geologists field conference, May 1980, Reno, Nevada, guidebook, p. 9-13.

Atwater, T., 1970, Implications of plate tectonics for the Cenozoic tectonic evolution of western North America: Geological Society of America Bulletin, v. 81, p. 3513-3535.

Axelrod, D.I., 1957, Late Tertiary floras and the Sierra Nevadan uplift: Geological Society of America Bulletin, v. 68, p. 19-46.

Axelrod, D.I., 1962, Post-Pliocene uplift of the Sierra Nevada, California: Geological Society of America Bulletin, v. 73, p. 183-198.

Axelrod, D.I., 1992, The middle Miocene flora of western Nevada: University of California Press, Geological Sciences, v. 137, 50 p., 18 pl.

Axelrod, D.I., and Ting, W.S., 1960, Late Pliocene floras east of the Sierra Nevada: California University Publication in the Geological Sciences, v. 39, no. 1, p. 1-118.

Bastin, E.S., 1922, Bonanza ores of the Comstock Lode, Virginia City, Nevada: U.S. Geological Survey Bulletin 735-C, p. 41-63.

Bateman, P., and Eaton, J.P., 1967, Sierra Nevada batholith: Science, v. 158, no. 3807, p. 1407-1417.

Bateman, P.E., and Wahrhaftig, C., 1966, Geology of the Sierra Nevada, in Bailey, E.H., ed., Geology of northern California: California Division of Mines and Geology Bulletin 190, p. 107-172.

Bateman, R.L., and Scheibach, R.B., 1975, Evaluation of geothermal activity in the Truckee Meadows, Washoe County, Nevada: Nevada Bureau of Mines and Geology Report 25, 44 p.

Becker, G.F., 1882, Geology of the Comstock Lode and the Washoe District: U.S. Geologic Survey Monograph 3.

Bell, E.J., 1978, Roadlog—Olinghouse Road to Silver Springs, in Western Basin and Range faulting: Seismological Society of America Annual Meeting, 73rd, April 1978, Reno, Nev guidebook, p. 7.

Bell, J.W., 1981, Quaternary fault map, Reno sheet: Nevada Bureau of Mines and Geology Map 79, scale 1:250,000.

Bell, J.W., and Bonham, H.F., Jr., 1987, Vista Quadrangle geologic map: Nevada Bureau of Mines and Geology Map 4Hg.

Bell, J.W., and Pease, R.C., 1980, Soil stratigraphy as a technique for fault activity assessment in the Carson City area, Nevada: U.S. Geological Survey Open-File Report 80-801, p. 577-600.

Bell, J.W., Ramelli, A.R., and Glancy, P.A., 1995, Quaternary geology, active faults, and land-slides—Reno to Genoa, Nevada: American Association of State Geologists Annual Meeting, Reno, June 1995, Road Log and Guidebook, 14 p.

Bell, J.W., Slemmons, D.B., and Wallace, R.E., 1984, Neotectonics of western Nevada and guide-book for selected Nevada earthquake areas, in Western geological excursions guidebook—Volume 4 (fieldtrip 18): Geological Society of America, Annual Meeting, November 1984, Reno, Nevada, guidebook, v. 4, p. 387-472.

Bensen, L.V., and Thompson, R.S., 1987, Lake-level variation in the Lahontan Basin for the past 50,000 years: Quaternary Research, v. 28, p. 69-85.

Best, M.G., Christensen, E.H., Deino, A.L., Grommé, C.S., McKee, E.H., and Noble, D.C., 1989, Excursion 3A: Eocene through Miocene volcanism in the Great Basin of the western United States: New Mexico Bureau of Mines and Mineral Resources Memoir 47, p. 91-133.

Bingler, E.C., 1974, Reno Quadrangle earthquake hazards map: Nevada Bureau of Mines and Geology Map 4Ai.

Bingler, E.C., 1975, Guidebook to the Quaternary geology along the western flank of the Truckee Meadows, Washoe County, Nevada: Nevada Bureau of Mines and Geology Report 22, 16 p.

Bingler, E.C., 1977, New Empire Quadrangle geologic map: Nevada Bureau of Mines and Geology Map 59.

Birkeland, P.W., 1963, Pleistocene volcanism and deformation of the Truckee area, north of Lake Tahoe, California: Geological Society of America, v. 74, p. 1453 -1464.

Birkeland, P.W., 1964, Pleistocene glaciation of the northern Sierra Nevada, north of Lake Tahoe, California: Journal of Geology, v. 72, p. 810-823

Birkeland, P.W., 1965, Roadlog—Reno to Mount Rose, Tahoe City, Truckee, and return, in Wahrhaftig, C., Morrison, R.B., and Birkeland, P.W., eds., Guidebook for Field Conference 1—Northern Great Basin and California: International Association for Quaternary Research, 7th Congress, p. 48-59.

Birkeland, P.W., 1966, Trip No. 4—Tertiary and Quaternary geology along the Truckee River with emphasis on the correlation of Sierra Nevada glaciation with fluctuation of Lake Lahontan, in Guidebook for field trip excursions in northern Nevada: Geological Society of America, 62nd., Cordilleran Section Meeting, Reno, Nevada, April 1966, p. D1-14, .

Birkeland, P.W., 1968, Mean velocities and boulder transport during Tahoe-age floods of the Truckee River, California-Nevada: Geological Society of America Bulletin, v. 79, p. 137-142.

Birkeland, P.W., 1968, Correlation of Quaternary stratigraphy of the Sierra Nevada with that of the Lake Lahontan area, in Morrison, R.B., and Wright, H.E., eds., Means of correlation of Quaternary successions: International Association of Quaternary Research, Proceedings, 7th Congress, U.S.A., 1965, v. 8, p. 469-500.

Birman, J.H., 1964, Glacial geology across the crest of the Sierra Nevada, California: Geological Society of America Special Paper 75.

Blackwelder, E.B., 1931, Pleistocene glaciation of the Sierra Nevada and basin ranges: Geological Society of America Bulletin, v. 42, p. 865-922.

Blackwelder, E.B., 1933, Eastern slope of the Sierra Nevada, in Middle California and western Nevada: 16th International Geological Congress, Guidebook 16, p. 81-95.

Bonham, H.F., Jr., and Bingler, E.C., 1973, Reno Quadrangle geologic map: Nevada Bureau of Mines and Geology Map 4Ag.

Bonham, H.F., Jr., and Burnett, J.L., 1976, South Lake Tahoe Quadrangle geologic map: Nevada Bureau of Mines and Geology Map 2Ag.

Bonham, H.F., Jr., and Papke, K.G., 1969, Geology and mineral deposits of Washoe and Storey Counties, Nevada: Nevada Bureau of Mines and Geology Bulletin 70, 152 p.

Bonham, H.F., Jr., and Rogers, D.K., 1983, Mount Rose NE Quadrangle geologic map: Nevada Bureau of Mines and Geology Map 4Bg.

Born, S.M., 1972, Late Quaternary history, deltaic sedimentation, and mudlump formation at Pyramid Lake, Nevada: Center for Water Resources Research, Desert Research Institute, University of Nevada, Reno, 97 p.

Born, S.M., and Ritter, D.F., 1970, Modern terrace development near Pyramid Lake, Nevada, and its geologic implications: Geological Society of America Bulletin, v. 81, p. 1233-1242.

Brice, J., 1960, Historical geology: Wm. C. Brown Co., Dubuque, Iowa, 174 p.

Broecker, W.S., and Kaufman, A., 1965, Radiocarbon chronology of Lake Lahontan and Lake Bonneville - II, Great Basin: Geological Society of America Bulletin, v. 76, p. 537-565.

Broecker, W.S., Kaufman, A., and Orr, P.C., 1958, Radiocarbon chronology of Lake Lahontan and Lake Bonneville: Geological Society of America Bulletin, v. 69, p. 537-566.

Burnett, J.L., 1967, Geologic map of Lake Tahoe, southern half: California Division of Mines and Geology open-file map.

Burnett, J.L., 1968, Geology of the Lake Tahoe Basin, in Evans, J.R., and Matthews, R.A., eds., Geologic studies in the Lake Tahoe area, California and Nevada: Geological Society of Sacramento Annual Field Trip Guidebook, 1968.

Burnett, J.L., 1971, Geology of the Lake Tahoe Basin: California Geology, v. 24, no. 7, p. 119-127.

Burnett, J.L., and Matthews, R.A., 1971, Geological look at Lake Tahoe: California Geology, v. 24, no. 7, p. 128-130.

California Department of Water Resources, 1991, Carson River Atlas: California Department of Water Resources, Sacramento, California, 132 p.

Calkins, F.C., 1944, Outline of the Comstock Lode district, Nevada: U.S. Geological Survey open-file report.

Carlson, H.S., 1974, Nevada place names: University of Nevada Press, Reno, Nevada, 282 p.

Christiansen, R.L., and Lipman, P.W., 1972, Cenozoic volcanism and plate-tectonic evolution of the western United States - II, late Cenozoic: Royal Society of London Philosophical Transactions, v. 271, p. 249-284.

Church, J.A., 1879, The Comstock Lode—its formation and history: John Wiley and Sons, New York.

Coats, R.R., 1940, Propylitization and related types of alteration on the Comstock Lode: Economic Geology, v. 35, p. 1-6.

Cooper, J.J., Thomas, R.O., and Reed, S.M., 1985, Total mercury in sediment, water, and fishes in the Carson River drainage, west-central Nevada: Division of Environmental Protection, Carson City, Nevada, 96 p.

Cordova, T., 1969, Active faults in Quaternary alluvium and seismic regionalism in a portion of the Mount Rose quadrangle, Nevada [M.S. thesis]: University of Nevada, Reno, 53 p.

Cox, A., Doell, R.R., and Dalrymple, G.B., 1963, Geomagnetic polarity epochs —Sierra Nevada II: Science, v. 142, p. 382-385.

Crippen, J.R., and Pavelka, B.R., 1970, The Lake Tahoe Basin, California-Nevada: U.S. Geological Survey Water-Supply Paper 1972, 56 p.

Dalrymple, G.B., 1963, Potassium-argon dates of some Cenozoic volcanic rocks of the Sierra Nevada, California: Geological Society of America Bulletin, v. 74, p. 379-390.

Dalrymple, G.B., 1964, Cenozoic chronology of the Sierra Nevada, California: University of California Publication in the Geological Sciences, v. 47, 41 p.

Earl, P.I., 1986, This was Nevada: Nevada Historical Society, Reno, 192 p.

Eaton, G.P., 1980, Geophysical and geological characteristics of the crust of the Basin and Range province, in Continental Tectonics: National Academy of Sciences, Washington, D.C., p. 96-113.

Eaton, G.P., 1982, The Basin and Range province—origin and tectonic significance: Earth and Planetary Sciences Annual Review, v. 10, p. 409-440.

Eaton, G.P., 1984, The Miocene Great Basin of western North America as an extending back-arc region: Tectonophysics, v. 102, p. 275-295.

Eaton, G.P., Wahl, R.R., Prostka, H.J., Mabey, D.R., and Kleinkopf, M.D., 1978, Regional gravity and tectonic patterns—their relation to late Cenozoic epeirogeny and lateral spreading in the western Cordillera, in Smith, R.B., and Eaton, G.P., eds., Cenozoic tectonics and regional geophysics of the western Cordillera: Geological Society of America Memoir 152, p. 51-92.

Farquhar, F.P., 1972, History of the Sierra Nevada: University of California Press, Berkeley, 262 p.

Firby, J.R., 1985, Self-guiding photo tour of geologic features of the Reno and Lake Tahoe areas, Nevada and California, in Field Trip Guide—The northern Sierra: National Association of Geology Teachers Far Western Section, University of Nevada, Reno, Oct. 4-6, 1985, p. 29-51.

Flint, R.F., 1967, Glacial and Pleistocene Geology: John Wiley and Sons, New York, 553 p.

Fullerton D.S., 1986, Chronology and correlation of glacial deposits in the Sierra Nevada, California, in Sibrava, V., Bowen, D.Q., and Richmond, G.M., eds., Quaternary glaciations in the Northern Hemisphere: Quaternary Science Reviews, v. 5, p. 161-169.

Galloway, J.D., 1947, Early engineering works contributory to the Comstock: Nevada Bureau of Mines and Geology Bulletin 45, 103 p.

Garside, L.J., 1979, Steamboat-Moana-Brady's roadlog: Geothermal Resources Council 1979 Annual Meeting, Reno, Nevada, Field Trip No. 4, 25 p.

Garside, L.J., and Schilling, J.H., 1979, Thermal waters of Nevada: Nevada Bureau of Mines and Geology Bulletin 91, 167 p.

Gates, W.C.B., and Watters, R.J., 1992, Geology of Reno and Truckee Meadows, Nevada, USA: Bulletin of the Association of Engineering Geologists, v. 29, no. 3, p. 229-298.

Gianella, V.P., 1933, Itinerary, Reno to Walley Hot Springs and return, *in* Middle California and western Nevada: International Geological Congress, 16th, Guidebook 16, Excursion C-1, p. 108-116.

Gianella, V.P., 1936, Geology of the Silver City district and the southern portion of the Comstock Lode, Nevada: Nevada Bureau of Mines and Geology Bulletin 29, 108 p.

Gianella, V.P., 1959, Period of mineralization of the Comstock Lode, Nevada [abs.]: Geological Society of America Bulletin, v. 70, no. 12, part 2, p. 1721-1722.

Gilbert, C.M., and Reynolds, M.W., 1973, Character and chronology of basin development, western margin of the Basin and Range province: Geological Society of America Bulletin, v. 84, p. 2489-2509.

Glancy, P.A., 1971, A reconnaissance of streamflow and fluvial sediment transport, Incline Village area, Lake Tahoe, Nevada—First Progress Report, 1970: Nevada Division of Water Resources Information Series Report 8.

Glancy, P.A., 1980, Streamflow, sediment transport, and nutrient transport at Incline Village, Lake Tahoe, Nevada, 1970-73: U.S. Geological Survey Open-File Report 80-2045.

Glancy, P.A., Harrill, J.R., Jacobson, R.L., and Mifflin, M.D., 1984, Guidebook for a field tour of the hydrogeology of the Carson and Truckee River basins, Nevada, *in* Western Geological Excursions Guidebook—v. 3 (Fieldtrip No. 4): Geological Society of America Annual Meeting, November 1984, Reno, Nevada, guidebook, v. 3, p. 55-146.

Glancy, P.A., and Katzer, T.L., 1977, Washoe City Quadrangle flood and related debris hazards map: Nevada Bureau of Mines and Geology Map 5Al.

Glass, A., and Glass, M.E., 1975, Western Nevada: Nevada Historical Society Guidebook Series, 51 p.

Grose, T.L.T., 1985, Glenbrook Quadrangle geologic map: Nevada Bureau of Mines and Geology Map 2Bg

Grose, T.L.T., 1986, Marlette Lake Quadrangle geologic map: Nevada Bureau of Mines and Geology Map 2Cg.

Hamlin, W.K., 1975, The Earth's Dynamic Systems: Burgess Publishing Co., Minneapolis, 578 p.

Harding, S.T., 1962, Evaporation from Pyramid and Winnemucca Lakes: American Society of Civil Engineers Proceedings, Journal of the Irrigation and Drainage Division, March 1962.

Hardman, G., and Venstrom, C., 1941, A one hundred year record of Truckee River run-off estimated from changes in levels and volumes of Pyramid and Winnemucca Lakes: American Geophysical Union Transactions, v. 22, p. 71-90.

Hill, M., 1975, Geology of the Sierra Nevada: University of California Press, Berkeley.

Houghton, J.G., Sakamoto, C.M., and Gifford, R.O., 1975, Nevada's weather and climate: Nevada Bureau of Mines and Geology Special Publication 2, 78 p.

Hudson, D.M., 1993, The Comstock district, Nevada, *in* Lahren, M.M., Trexler, J.H., Jr., and Spinosa, C., eds., Crustal evolution of the Great Basin and the Sierra Nevada: Geological Society of America, Cordilleran/Rocky Mountain Sections meeting, University of Nevada, May 1993, Reno, Nevada, p. 481-496.

Hudson, D.M., and Carr, T., 1987, Field Trip No. 11—Comstock Lode/Steamboat Springs precious metals deposits, Nevada, *in* Bulk mineable precious metal deposits of the western United States: Symposium of the Geological Society of Nevada, April 1987, Reno, Nevada, field trip guidebook. p. 395-413.

Hudson, F.S., 1960, Post-Pliocene uplift of the Sierra Nevada, California: Geological Society of America Bulletin, v. 71, p. 1547-1574.

Hunt, C.B., 1967, Basin and Range province, *in* Physiography of the United States: W.H. Freeman, San Francisco.

Hyne, N.J., Chelminski,P., Court, J.E., Gorsline, D.S., and Goldman, C.R., 1972, Quaternary history of Lake Tahoe, California-Nevada: Geological Society of America Bulletin, v. 83, p. 1435-1448.

James, J.W., 1980, Lake Tahoe field trip guide: Association of Pacific Coast Geographers 43rd Annual Meeting, June 1980, Reno, Nevada, 17 p.

Jones, J.C., and Gianella, V.P., 1933, Excursion C-1—Reno and vicinity, *in* Middle California and western Nevada: International Geological Congress, 16th, 1933, Guidebook 16, p. 96-102.

Katzer, T.L., and Schroer, C.V., 1981, Carson City Quadrangle flood and related debris flow hazards map: Nevada Bureau of Mines and Geology Map 1Al.

Knudson, T., 1994, Lake Tahoe clarity takes turn for worse: Reno Gazette- Journal, December 25, 1994.

Lanner, R.M., 1981, The piñon pine—a natural and cultural history: University of Nevada Press, Reno, 208 p.

Lanner, R.M., 1984, Trees of the Great Basin: University of Nevada Press, Reno, Nevada, 215 p.

Larson, E.R., and Beal, L.H., 1966, Trip No. 2—Mining areas in western Nevada, in Guidebook for field trip excursions in northern Nevada: Geological Society of America, Cordilleran Section meeting, April 1966, Reno, Nevada. p. B1-3.

Larson, E.R., and Bonham, H.F., Jr., eds., 1968, Field trip roadlog to Steamboat Springs, the Comstock Lode, and the Dayton iron deposit: Geological Society of Nevada field trip, April 1968, Reno, Nevada, 6 p.

Lawson, A.C., 1912, The recent fault scarps at Genoa, Nevada: Seismological Society of America Bulletin, v. 2, no. 3, p. 193-200.

Lekisch, B., 1988, Tahoe place names: Great West Books, Lafayette, California.

Lintz, J, Jr., ed., 1965, First Basin and Range geology field conference guidebook: Mackay School of Mines at the University of Nevada, Reno, and the National Science Foundation, p. 17-13 thru 18-4.

Lintz, J., Jr., 1993, Lake Tahoe field trip, in Lahren, M.M., Trexler, J.H., Jr. and Spinosa, C., eds., Crustal evolution of the Great Basin and Sierra Nevada: Geological Society of America Guidebook, Cordilleran/Rocky Mountain Section Meeting, University of Nevada, Reno, May 19-21, p. 263-276.

Lipman, P.W., Prostka, H.J., and Christiansen, R.L., 1972, Cenozoic volcanism and plate-tectonic evolution of the western United States. 1. Early and middle Cenozoic: Royal Society of London Philosophical Transactions, v. 271, p. 217-248.

Livaccari, R.F., 1979, Late Cenozoic tectonic evolution of the western United States: Geology, v. 7, p. 72-75.

Lord, E., 1883, Comstock mining and miners: U.S. Geological Survey Monograph 4, Howell-North Books, San Diego, California.

Louderback, G.D., 1907, General geologic features of the Truckee region east of the Sierra Nevada: Geological Society of America Bulletin, v. 18, p. 662-669.

Louderback, G.D., 1911, Lake Tahoe, California-Nevada: Journal of Geography, v. 9, p. 227-279.

Louderback, G.D., 1923, Basin Range structure in the Great Basin: University of California Publication in the Geological Sciences, v. 14, p. 329-376.

Louderback, G.D., 1924, Period of scarp production in the Great Basin: University of California Publication in the Geological Sciences, v. 15, p. 1-44.

Lovejoy, E.M.P., 1969, Mount Rose, northern Carson Range, Nevada—New light on the late Cenozoic tectonic history of the Sierra Nevada from a classic locality: Geological Society of America Bulletin, v. 50, p. 1833-1942.

Lydon, P.A., 1962, Geological history of the northern Sierra Nevada: Geological Society of Sacramento Annual Field Trip Guidebook, p. 4-30.

Mariner, R.H., Rapp, J.B., Willey, L.M., and Presser, T.S., 1974, Chemical composition and estimated minimum thermal reservoir temperatures of the principal hot springs of northern and central Nevada: U.S. Geological Survey Open-File Report, 32 p.

Matthes. F.E., 1942, Glaciers, in Hydrology (Physics of the Earth, 9): McGraw-Hill, New York, p. 149-219.

Matthews, R.A., 1968, Geologic map of the Lake Tahoe Basin, northern half: California Division of Mines and Geology Open-File Report, 9 p.

Matthews, R.A., and Burnett, J.L., 1971, Geology for land use planning in the Lake Tahoe Basin, California: Geology and geomorphology of the Lake Tahoe region—a guide for planning (prepared for the Tahoe Regional Planning Agency and the U.S. Department of Agriculture Forest Service).

McDonald, D., 1982, Virginia City and the silver region of the Comstock Lode: Nevada Publications, Las Vegas, 128 p.

McKee, E.H., 1971, Tertiary igneous chronology of the Great Basin of western United States— implications for tectonic models: Geological Society of America Bulletin, v. 82, p. 3497-3502.

Meeuwig, R.O., Budy, J.D., and Everett, R.L., 1990, Pinus monophylla Torr. & Frém, Singleleaf pinyon, in Silvics of North America: Forest Service, U.S. Department of Agriculture, Agricultural Handbook, v. 1, Conifers, p. 380-384.

Mifflin, M.D., and Wheat, M.M., 1979, Pluvial lakes and estimated pluvial climates of Nevada: Nevada Bureau of Mines and Geology Bulletin 94, 57 p.

Miller, J.R., Lechler, P.J., and Rowland, J., 1993, Heavy metal transport by physical processes in the Carson River valley, west-cental Nevada, USA: Implications to the distribution and storage of metal pollutants in tropical environments: Proceedings Perspectives for Environmental Geochemistry in Tropical Countries, Niteroi, Brazil.

Moore, J.G., and Archbold, N.L., 1969, Geology and mineral deposits of Lyon, Douglas, and Ormsby Counties, Nevada: Nevada Bureau of Mines and Geology Bulletin 75, 53 p.

Morrison, R.B., 1964, Lake Lahontan—geology of southern Carson Desert, Nevada: U.S. Geological Survey Professional Paper 401, 155 p.

Morrison, R.B., 1965, Quaternary geology of the Great Basin, in Wright, H.E., Jr., and Frey, D., eds., The Quaternary of the United States (revised volume for the International Association of Quaternary Research, VII Congress): Princeton University Press, Princeton, New Jersey, P. 265-285.

Morrison, R.B., 1991, Quaternary stratigraphic, hydrologic, and climatic history of the Great Basin, with emphasis on Lakes Lahontan, Bonneville, and Tecopa, in Morrison, R.B., ed., Quaternary nonglacial geology, conterminous U.S.: Geological Society of America, The Geology of North America, v. K-2, p. 283-320.

Morrison, R.B., and Davis, J.O., 1984, Quaternary stratigraphy and archeology of the Lake Lahontan area, a re-assessment, in Western Geological Excursions Guidebook—v. 1 (Fieldtrip 13): Geological Society of America Annual Meeting, 1984, Reno, Nevada, guidebook, p. 252-281.

Morrison, R.B., and Frye, J.C., 1965, Correlation of the middle and late Quaternary succession of the Lake Lahontan, Lake Bonneville, Rocky Mountain (Wasatch Range), southern Great Plains, and eastern Midwest areas: Nevada Bureau of Mines and Geology Report 9, 51 p.

Mozingo, H.N., 1987, Shrubs of the Great Basin: University of Nevada Press, Reno, 342 p.

Myrick, D.F., 1962, Railroads of Nevada and eastern California—v. 1: Howell-North Books, Berkeley, p. 136-162.

Nolan, T.B., 1943, The Basin and Range province in Utah, Nevada, and California: U.S. Geological Survey Professional Paper 197-D, p. D141-196.

Paher, S.W., 1970, Nevada ghost towns and mining camps: Howell-North Books, Berkeley, California, 492 p.

Paher, 1972, Ponderosa country—a scenic and historic guide to Reno and vicinity: Nevada Publications, Las Vegas, Nevada, 48 p.

Pease, R.C., 1979, Scarp degradation and fault history near Carson City, Nevada [M.S. thesis]: University of Nevada, Reno, 95 p.

Pease, R.C., 1979, Genoa Quadrangle earthquake hazards map: Nevada Bureau of Mines and Geology Map 1Ci.

Pease, R.C., 1980, Genoa Quadrangle geologic map: Nevada Bureau of Mines and Geology Map 1Cg.

Ramelli, A.R., 1992, Seismic hazards of the Reno/Carson City/Lake Tahoe aresa. in Western states seismic policy council, XV Annual Meeting, Field trip guide, October 1992, 34 p.

Reno Gazette-Journal, 1995, Researchers link coastal motorists to Tahoe's clarity: Reno Gazette-Journal, June 10, 1995.

Rose, R.L., 1966, Trip No. 2—Cenozoic geology of the lower Truckee canyon, in Guidebook for field-trip excursions in northern Nevada: Geological Society of America, Cordilleran Section meeting, April 1966, Reno, Nevada, guidebook, P. C1-6.

Rose, R.L., 1969, Geology of parts of the Wadsworth and Churchill Butte Quadrangles, Nevada: Nevada Bureau of Mines and Geology Bulletin 71, 29 p.

Russell, I.C., 1885, Geological history of Lake Lahontan: U.S. Geological Survey Monograph 11, 288 p.

Ryall, A.S., 1977, Earthquake hazard in the Nevada region: Seismological Society of America Bulletin, v. 67, no. 2, p. 517-532.

Ryall, A., Slemmons, D.B., and Gedney, L.D., 1966, Seismicity, tectonism, and surface faulting in the western United States during historic time: Seismological Society of America Bulletin, v. 56, p. 1105-1135.

Ryall, A.S., and VanWormer, J.D., 1980, Estimation of maximum magnitude and recommended seismic zone changes in the western Great Basin: Seismological Society of America Bulletin, v. 70, no. 5, p. 1573-1581.

Sanders, C., and Slemmons, D.B., 1978, Sparks-Wadsworth area roadlog, *in* Western Basin and Range active faulting: Seismological Society of America Annual Meeting, 73rd, April 1978, Reno, Nevada, guidebook, p. 3-6.

Saucedo, G.J., and Wagner, D.L., 1992, Geologic map of the Chico Quadrangle: California Division of Mines and Geology, Regional Geologic Map Series, No 7A.

Schoen, R., and White, D.E., 1965, Hydrothermal alteraton in GS-3 and GS-4 drill holes, Main Terrace, Steamboat Springs, Nevada: Economic Geology, v. 60, no. 7, p. 1411-1421.

Schweickert, R.A., and Firby, J.R., 1985, The northern Sierra Nevada and self-guiding photo tour of geologic features of the Reno and Lake Tahoe areas, Nevada and California: National Association of Teachers, Far Western Section, Fall Meeting, October 1985, Mackay School of Mines, University of Nevada, Reno.

Shamberger, H.A., 1972, The story of the water supply for the Comstock: U.S. Geological Survey Professional Paper 779, 52 p.

Sharp, R.P., and Birman, J.H., 1963, Additions to classical sequence of Pleistocene glaciations, Sierra Nevada, California: Geological Society of America Bulletin, v. 74, p. 1079-1086.

Shearman, D.J., McGugan, A., Stein, C., and Smith, A.J., 1989, Ikaite, $CaCO_3 \cdot 6H_2O$, precursor of the thinolites in the Quaternary tufas and tufa mounds of the Lahontan and Mono Lake basins, western United States: Geological Society of America Bulletin, v. 101, p. 913-917.

Shutler, R., Jr., 1961, Correlation of beach terraces with climatic cycles of pluvial Lake Lahontan, Nevada: Annals of the New York Academy of Sciences, v. 95, Article 1, p. 513-520.

Silberman, M.L., and McKee, E.H., 1972, A summary of radiometric age determinations on Tertiary volcanic rocks from Nevada and eastern California—Part II, western Nevada: Isochron/West, no. 4, p. 7-28.

Silberman, M.L., Stewart, J.H., and McKee, E.H., 1976, Igneous activity, tectonics, and hydrothermal precious-metal mineralization in the Great Basin during Cenozoic time: Society of Mining Engineers Transactions, v. 260, p. 253-263.

Silberman, M.L., White, D.E., Keith, T.E.C., and Docktar, R.D., 1979, Limits on the duration of hydrothermal activity at Steamboat Springs, Nevada, by K-Ar ages of spatially associated volcanic rocks: U.S. Geological Survey Professional Paper 458-D, 14 p.

Slemmons, D.B., 1967, Pliocene and Quaternary crustal movements of the Basin and Range province, U.S.A., *in* Sea level changes and crustal movements of the Pacific: Journal of Geoscience, Osaka City University, v. 10, p. 90-103.

Slemmons, D.B., 1977, Field trip guide to Carson Valley, Genoa, Carson City, Silver City, Virginia City, and Reno, Nevada: Rock Mechanics Symposium, 19th, Mackay School of Mines, University of Nevada, Reno, 22 p.

Slemmons, D.B., Jones, A.E., and Gimlett, J.I., 1965, Catalog of Nevada earthquakes, 1852-1960: Seismological Society of America Bulletin, v. 55, no. 2, p. 519-565.

Slemmons, D.B., Lintz, J., Jr., and Jones, A.E., 1966, Geological road guide—Junction U.S. 50 and U.S. 395 in Carson Valley, *in* Evans, J.R., ed., Guidebook along the east-central front of the Sierra Nevada: Geological Society of Sacramento Annual Field Trip, June 1966.

Smith, A.M., 1932, The mines and mills of Silver City, Nevada: Nevada Bureau of Mines and Geology Bulletin 15, 28 p.

Smith, G.H., 1943, The history of the Comstock Lode, 1850-1920: Nevada Bureau of Mines and Geology Bulletin 37, 318 p.

Soeller, S.A., and Nielsen, R.L., 1980, Reno NW Quadrangle geologic map: Nevada Bureau of Mines and Geology Map 4Dg.

Stewart, J.H., 1980, Geology of Nevada: Nevada Bureau of Mines and Geology Special Publication 4, 136 p.

Stewart, J.H., and Carlson, J.E., 1978, Geologic map of Nevada: U.S. Geological Survey, scale 1:500,000.

Suppe, J., Powell, C., and Berry, R., 1975, Regional topography, seismicity, Quaternary volcanism, and the present-day tectonics of the western United States: American Journal of Science, v. 275A, p. 397-436.

Sutro, A., 1868, The mineral resources of the United States and the importance and necessity of inaugurating a rational system of mining, with special reference to the Comstock Lode and the Sutro Tunnel, in Nevada: John Murphy and Company, Baltimore.

Tabor, R.W., and Ellen, S., 1975, Washoe City Quadrangle geologic map: Nevada Bureau of Mines and Geology Map 5Ag.

Tabor, R.W., Ellen, S., and Clark, M.M., 1978, Washoe City Quadrangle geologic hazards map: Nevada Bureau of Mines and Geology Map 5An.

Tabor, R.W., Ellen, S.E., Clark, M.M., Glancy, P.A., and Katzer, T.L., 1983, Geology, geophysics, geologic hazards, and engineering and geologic character of earth materials in the Washoe Lake area—text to accompany map of the Environmental Series, Washoe City Quadrangle, Nevada: Nevada Bureau of Mines and Geology Open-File Report 83-7, 91 p.

Tahoe Regional Planning Agency and Forest Service, U.S. Department of Agriculture, 1971, Geology and geomorphology of the Lake Tahoe region—a guide for planning: Tahoe Regional Planning Agency and Forest Service, U.S. Department of Agriculture, South Lake Tahoe, California, open-file report.

Thompson, G.A., 1956, Geology of the Virginia City Quadrangle, Nevada: U.S. Geological Survey Bulletin 1042-C, 77 p.

Thompson, G.A., 1967, The rift system of the western United States, in The World Rift System—International Upper Mantle Commission Symposium: Canada Geological Survey Paper 66-14, p. 280-290.

Thompson, G.A., 1972, Cenozoic Basin Range tectonism in relation to deep structure: International Geological Congress, 24th, Montreal, 1972, Proceedings, p. 84-90.

Thompson, G.A., and Sandberg, C.H., 1958, Structural significance of gravity surveys in the Virginia City-Mount Rose area, Nevada and California: Geological Society of America Bulletin, v. 69, p. 1269-1282.

Thompson, G.A., and White, D.E., 1964, Regional geology of the Steamboat Springs area, Washoe County, Nevada: U.S. Geological Survey Professional Paper 458-A, 52 p.

Tingley, J.V., and Bonham, H.F., Jr., 1984, SEG precious metals field trip: Society of Economic Geologists, Fall 1984 Road Log/Trip Guide, p. 1-5.

Townley, J.M., 1983, Tough Little Town on the Truckee: Reno, 1868-1900: Jamison Station Press, Reno, 286 p.

Townley, J.M., 1984, The Comstock guidebook: Jamison Station Press, Reno, 26 p.

Townley, J.M., 1984, The Pyramid Lake Indian War: Jamison Station Press, Reno, 22 p.

Townley, J.M., 1985, The Pony Express guidebook: Jamison Station Press, Reno, Nevada, 57 p.

Trexler, D.T., 1977, Carson City Quadrangle geologic map: Nevada Bureau of MInes and Geology Map 1Ag.

Trexler, D.T. and Bell, J.W., 1979, Carson City Quadrangle earthquake hazards map: Nevada Bureau of Mines and Geology Map 1Ai

Trexler, D.T., and Pease, R.C., 1981, Geologic mapping of the Vista and Steamboat quadrangles, Nevada: U.S. Geological Survey Open-File Report 81-832, 32 p.

Twain, Mark, 1872, 1962, Roughing it: New American Library, New York, 446 p.

U.S. Geological Survey, 1870-1880, Geological exploration of the fortieth parallel (King Survey): Government Printing Office, Washington, D.C., v. 3, Mining Industry, 1870, v. 4, Zoology and Paleontology, 1877.

VanWormer, J.D., and Ryall, A.S., 1980, Sierra Nevada-Great Basin boundary zone—earthquake hazard related to structure, active tectonic processes, and anomalous patterns of earthquake occurrences: Seismological Society of America Bulletin, v. 70, no. 5, p. 1557-1572.

Von Richtofen, F.B., 1866, The Comstock Lode, its character and the probable mode of its continuance in depth: Sutro Tunnel Company, Towne & Bacon, San Francisco.

Wahrhaftig, C., and Curtis, G.H., 1965, Reno, Lake Tahoe, Sayles Flat, Hope Valley, Coleville, Sonora Pass Junction, California, in Wahrhaftig, C., Morrison, R.B., and Birkeland, P.W., eds., Guidebook for Field Conference 1—Northern Great Basin and California: International Association for Quaternary Research, 7th Congress, p. 59-70.

Waibel, A.F., 1983, Field Trip No. 1—Reno, Nevada to Dixie Valley, Nevada, in Symposium on the role of heat in the development on energy and mineral resources in the northern Basin and Range province: Geothermal Resources Council and American Association of Petroleum Geologists Annual Meeting, May 1983, Reno, Nevada, p. 1-3.

Wallace, R.E., 1978, Geometry and rates of change of fault-generated range faults, north-central Nevada: U.S. Geological Survey Journal of Research, v. 6, p. 637-650.

Watters, R.J., 1984, Engineering geology of the Slide Mountain rockslide and water flood-debris flow, in Western Geological Excursions Guidebook (Fieldtrip 12): Geological Society of America Annual Meeting, November 1984, Reno, Nevada, guidebook, v. 2, p. 88-95.

Weimer, B.S., 1987, Geologic roadlogs—Reno-Steamboat Springs; Steamboat-Virginia City-Carson City-Steamboat; Steamboat-Carson City-Carson Valley Daggett Pass-Lake Tahoe-Mount Rose Summit-Steamboat; and Reno-Wadsworth-Pyramid Lake-Reno, 79 p.

Weimer, B.S., 1987, Reno-Virginia City-Carson City-Washoe Valley-Steamboat Roadlog, in Mining history and place names of the Comstock area:11th Annual Western States Geographical Names Conference, September 19, 1987, field trip guidebook, 35 p.

Weissburg, B.C., Browne, P.R.L., and Seward, T.M., 1979, Ore metals in active geothermal systems, in Barnes, H.L., ed., Geochemistry of hydrothermal ore deposits, 2nd edition: John Wiley and Sons, New York, p. 738-780.

Wheat, M.M., 1967, Survival arts of the primitive Paiutes: University of Nevada Press, Reno, 117 p.

Wheeler, S.S., 1982, The Nevada desert: The Caxton Printers, Caldwell, Idaho, 168 p.

White, D.E., 1967, Mercury and base-metal deposits with associated thermal and mineral waters, in Barnes, H.L., ed., Geochemistry of hydrothermal ore deposits: Holt, Rinehart, and Winston, Inc., New York, p. 575-631.

White, D.E., 1968, Hydrology, activity, and heat flow of the Steamboat Springs thermal system, Washoe County, Nevada: U.S. Geological Survey Professional Paper 458-C., 109 p.

White, D.E., 1980, Steamboat Springs geothermal area, in Epithermal ore deposits of northwestern Nevada: U.S. Geological Survey and Society of Economic Geologists field conference, May 1980, Reno, Nevada, guidebook, p. 44-51.

White, D.E., 1980, Roadlog—Steamboat Springs geothermal area, in Epithermal ore deposits of northwestern Nevada: U.S. Geological Survey and Society of Economic Geologists field conference, May 1980, Reno, Nevada, guidebook, p. 3-8.

White, D.E., 1983, Field Trip No. 2—Summary of Steamboat Springs geothermal area, Nevada with attached road-log commentary, in A Symposium on the role of heat in the development of energy and mineral resources in the northern Basin and Range province: Geothermal Resources Council and American Association of Petroleum Geologists Annual Meeting, May 1983, Reno, Nevada, guidebook, 22 p.

White, D.E., 1985, Summary of the Steamboat Springs geothermal area, Nevada, with attached road-log commentary, in Tooker, E.W., ed., Geologic characteristics of sediment- and volcanic-hosted disseminated gold deposits—search for an occurrence model: U.S. Geological Survey Bulletin 1646, p. 79-88.

White, D.E., Thompson, G.A., and Sandberg, C.H., 1964, Rocks, structure, and geologic history of Steamboat Springs thermal area, Washoe County, Nevada: U.S. Geological Survey Professional Paper 458-B, 63 p.

Whitebread, D.H., 1976, Alteration and geochemistry of Tertiary volcanic rocks in parts of the Virginia City quadrangle, Nevada: U.S. Geological Survey Professional Paper 936.

Whitebread, D.H., and Hoover, D.B., 1968, Preliminary results of geological, geochemical, and geophysical studies in part of the Virginia City quadrangle, Nevada: U.S. Geological Survey Circular 596, 20 p.

Wolfe, J., 1968, Earthquake history near Lake Tahoe, in Evans, J.R., and Matthews, R.A., eds., Geological studies in the Lake Tahoe area, California and Nevada: Geological Society of Sacramento Annual Field Trip, 1968, guidebook, p. 27-36.

Wright, L.A., 1976, Late Cenozoic fault patterns and stress fields in the Great Basin and westward displacement of the Sierra Nevada block: Geology, v. 4, p. 489-494.

Young, G.J., 1909, The ventilating-system at the Comstock mines, Nevada: Nevada Bureau of Mines and Geology Bulletin 3, p. 955-1009.

Zoback, M.L., Anderson, R.E., and Thompson, G.A., 1981, Cenozoic evolution of the state of stress and style of tectonism of the Basin and Range province of the western United States, in Vine, F.J., and Smith, A.G., organizers, Extensional tectonics associated with convergent plate boundaries: Royal Society of London, p. 189-216.

Virginia City in 1967.